W9-ADI-013
Ex Libris
John S. Ironside

PORTRAITS from a Chinese Scroll

盧傅志清著

Elizabeth Foreman Lewis

To dear Sally
from
Louise
February 26, 1944

PORTRAITS from a Chinese Scroll

by
Elizabeth Foreman Lewis

Illustrations by Virginia Hollinger Stout
Calligraphy by Chen Chao-ming

THE JOHN C. WINSTON COMPANY
Chicago Philadelphia Toronto

PRINTED IN THE U. S. A.
FIRST EDITION

Portraits from a Chinese Scroll

To my uncle
Louis Le franc
and
To the memory of my father and father-in-law

Joseph Francis Foreman
Wilson Seeley Lewis

"Great in spirit, broad in sympathies"

CALLIGRAPHY BY CHEN CHAO-MING

Head of Chinese Classics Department, Hwa Nan College, Foochow, China, 1912–1920. Instructor of Chinese Literature and Language at Johns Hopkins University, 1920–1925.

霍林路繪圖

Illustrations have been drawn from several years observation and drawings made in China by Virginia Hollinger Stout.

PORTRAITS

And the Great Khan told these ambassadors: "I had far liever hearken about the strange things, and the manners of the different countries you have seen, than merely be told of the business you went upon."

—*Messer Marco Polo*

THE MERCHANT

In every transaction, though it be small as a fly's head, the merchant seeks profit.

商賈爭蠅頭之利 古諺

You must know that the city of Cambaluc has such a multitude of houses, and such a vast population inside the walls and outside, that it seems quite past all possibility. . . . In the suburbs lodge the foreign merchants and travelers, of whom there are always great numbers who have come to bring presents to the Emperor, or to sell articles at court, or because the city affords so good a mart to attract traders.

To this city also are brought articles of greater cost and rarity, and in greater abundance of all kinds, than to any other city in the world. For people of every description, and from every region, bring things, including all the costly wares of India, as well as the fine and precious goods of Cathay itself with its provinces, some for the sovereign, some for the court, some for the city which is so great, some for the crowds of barons and knights, some for the great hosts of the Emperor which are quartered round about; and thus between court and city the quantity brought in is endless. As a sample, I tell you, no day in the year passes that there do not enter the city one thousand cart loads of silk alone. . . .

商賈爭蠅頭之利古諺

THE MERCHANT

Round about Cambaluc there are some two hundred other cities at various distances, from which traders come to sell their goods and buy others for their lords; and all find means to make their sales and purchases so that the traffic of the city is passing great.

—*Travels of Marco Polo*

Long centuries before Kubla Khan elected to make Cambaluc his capital city, the merchants of China, dealing not only in the necessaries of life but in luxuries with which most of the world was still unfamiliar, had become masters of the trading art. Many of these, accustomed to traveling from one end of the Middle Kingdom to the other and to far-distant vassal states as well, learned to face not only the usual lively dangers of the road, but also active persecution from resident trade interests in the towns and cities visited on their journeys. To ameliorate this last condition, provincial guild houses were erected in all important mercantile centers, and when a Foochow trader, for instance, was received inimically by some northern market, he could soon find shelter, protection, and assistance in the Fukien Merchant's Guild where those of his own province assembled. The actual trading, however, was the individual's problem, and failure after expensive and arduous journeying was not to be considered.

THE MERCHANT

商賈爭蠅頭之利
古諺

Accordingly, in the early eighteen hundreds when American clippers, with swift, white wings cleaving the horizon, set sail for that fabulous land of tea and silk and spice known as Cathay, their hard-headed Yankee captains found themselves, on arrival at Pagoda Anchorage or Canton, confronted by bartering sagacity that left them even more tight-lipped than usual. Only after the bitter and unexpected experience of being severely worsted in trade did these New England seafarers awake to the inherent ability of the suave and gracious Orientals with whom they were dealing. Here were adversaries who had at their command every trick common to bargaining plus a few special ones on the side, and the stranger was hard pressed to exchange profitably the cargo brought from Gloucester or New Bedford for the ginger, brocades, and ivory he wished to carry home.

Even today when all the world seeks the China trade, the foreigner, in order to be successful, must recognize first of all that the Chinese merchant is a born psychologist. The prospective customer, treated as a guest, finds himself sipping tea and discussing everything (save the business in mind) from weather to international affairs. Meanwhile his host is arriving at personal conclusions about the other's mental equipment. Should this denote gullibility and a carelessness

商賈爭蠅頭之利古諺

in spending, the proprietor of the establishment wastes little more time. He promptly displays his poorest quality stock and for it demands an exorbitant price.

If, on the other hand, he reaches the decision that his opponent "was not born yesterday," the deal progresses in a very different manner. For in trade, as in every other phase of Chinese existence, possession of brains is respected beyond all other qualities. Hidden treasures, which the favored only are permitted to view, are now brought forth one by one and, with allowance made for the customary sliding scale used in mercantile affairs "east of Suez," are reasonably priced. Where the proposed purchase is a real *objet d'art*, still another factor enters the transaction, for the Chinese dealer often has a highly developed aesthetic sense which, on occasion, impels him to lose a sale rather than to have beauty fall into unappreciative hands.

It is in the smaller, everyday affairs, however, that the contest of wits becomes free entertainment for all who are privileged to watch. Exercising the racial flair for dramatics, the merchant appeals to the crowd gathered before the open shop front to confirm his reputation for fair dealing, the unusual value of the article under discussion, and the fact that to lower the price in this instance would leave him a broken and a bankrupt man. The customer replies in kind, and not until after prolonged and vivid argument when, for example, the proprietor refuses to accept less than seventy-five cents for goods originally priced at one dollar and the buyer determines to limit his figure to sixty, is an *impasse* reached.

With an expression of sad tolerance for a world in which real bargains are unappreciated, the shopkeeper now wraps up the disputed object and puts it away. Often the act of withdrawal achieves what other methods have failed to do; namely, to settle the deal. If this ruse, however, does not succeed and the other participant walks away empty-handed, he is likely to be overtaken at the end of the street by a breathless clerk who informs him that his master, rather than see a patron go away dissatisfied, will sacrifice and consummate the sale for the amount offered. Surprisingly, this loss is sometimes only too real, for in cases where the customer is one of years' standing whom it would be foolish to offend, or a newcomer likely to return, the tradesman is willing to risk the present for the future.

Pasted on the walls of Chinese business establishments there is to be found the image of the God of Wealth, or the symbolic characters, virtue, integrity, and happiness, written on red paper. On occasion candles and incense are burned before these, and whether

商賈爭蠅頭之利古諺

商賈爭蠅頭之利 古諺

or not this tribute to high-mindedness influences all affairs under the roof, it is certainly true that the average tradesman, regardless of the tricks to which he may have resorted in preliminaries, will abide faithfully by the terms of final agreement. At this point, his word becomes as good as his bond, and literally so, for in many instances contracts never know the seal of writing. "Face," which affects so many facets of China's existence, assumes marked importance where business reputation is concerned, and foreigners have learned to depend on the Chinese custom of delivering in full value what was promised on the original order.

In large firms particularly, those responsible will make almost any sacrifice to save prestige, and when failure threatens an individual banking house, for instance, competitive institutions frequently rush to the rescue with sufficient funds to tide over the difficulty. If the worst happens, however, the depositor, unlike his counterpart in Europe and America, finds it possible to retrieve some of his losses by seizure of the bank's physical properties. Furniture and decorations, the very joists and rafters in the building, may all be removed by the investor-victim to the equivalent of his account on the books.

For most business transactions in China, there are three days of settlement in a year, with the third and final on New Year's. This last date is irrevocable and the man who cannot make arrangements to take care of his creditors at that time is ruined. While flight or suicide is sometimes resorted to in such instances, these acts are accompanied by such loss of "face" to the members of the family who remain that they are indulged in only by the most desperate.

Bound by these financial laws and faced constantly by the ill-fortunes of war, famine, and flood, the Chinese merchant finds his ability taxed to the utmost. That in spite of apparently insurmountable difficulties, he succeeds in conducting most of his affairs with dignity and integrity has been proved through the centuries not only by the respect which foreigners in his homeland accord him, but also by the world's electing him to manage financial affairs of importance in all the far-flung, lonely outposts of civilization.

In *Gift to the Chinese Air Force from Japan*, the characterization of the merchant is not an individual portrait drawn from life. It is rather a composite of business men to be seen everywhere in Peiping, Foochow, and Chungking, and in thousands of other towns and cities throughout Cathay. Shrewd, cautious, and untiring in effort, such men spend their lives trying to amass sufficient silver to care for their families and to give honor to their ancestors, for in China earning a

商賈爭蠅頭之利
古諺

商賈爭蠅頭之利
古諺

livelihood is never an end in itself, but rather the means of achieving security, reputation, and leisure in which to pursue the art of living. When, as in Wang Merchant's case, motivation is suddenly destroyed, the acute and experienced trader fades into the background, leaving in his place only a disarmed and stricken victim of personal grief.

霍林路

GIFT TO THE CHINESE AIR FORCE FROM JAPAN

Act I: Scene I

The small, still form lay in the study where the coolies had first carried it. One tightly ribboned ankle pressed flat the gathered folds of the material which rose above the band on the other leg; from slender, brown wrists delicate fingers hung relaxed and a glint of eye showed deceptively beneath folded lids, much as though the sleeper were on the verge of waking. To what had so recently happened, no clue except the dark, spreading stains on the satin jacket, remained.

Lin Scholar, continuing to stand transfixed a few feet away, stared at the prostrate figure and refused to believe what he saw. In another moment Small Wang would move and this horror now beating on consciousness would pass as did any other nightmare, given time. An hour earlier in this very room, the boy had been seated opposite him at the table beneath the oiled-paper windowlight. Together, they had considered in a page of history the foolishness of war and the evil ambitions of the men who waged it. Small Wang had listened somewhat inattentively. Throughout his short existence he had been familiar with advancing and retreating troops—what child of the Middle Kingdom was not? Occasionally one was frightened by soldiers, but the usual attitude of youth toward the Military was that borrowed from elders, a disdain centuries old.

Today with lessons ended, the lad had gone to his play and had swiftly forgotten so serious a subject in the greater attraction of flying a kite on the grave-dotted meadows outside the city. The spring wind had tugged gustily at the toy, tempting it up and onward until the paper dragon rose high above the boundary of an internationally disputed stretch of territory. Forgetful of danger and deaf to warning shouts from the servant who accompanied him, Small Wang sped in swift pursuit, skilfully reeling and tautening cord as he followed his kite over the forbidden border line. A dozen paces along he paused and glanced calculatingly at the symbolic black and gold monster now struggling with increasing vigor to reach farther heights of cloud-flecked blue. Suddenly a sharp sound crackled over the meadow and the young kite flyer, with a startled gesture of opening fist, crumpled to the earth. At once the dragon leaped into the freedom of cold space, but the boy, victim of an over-zealous Japanese sentry, continued to lie still with a bullet-shaped period accurately placed on the brief, written record of his life.

A foreign soldier's rifle shot! At repetition of this thought, anger began to cut through Lin Scholar's paralyzing inertia. During six years of teaching under this roof, he had tried to direct the pliable young mind in paths of tolerance. No man was entirely bad, he had taught, not even the unfathomable strangers from beyond the seas. True, between the Sons of Han and these others, whether the stocky dwarfs from islands near-by, or the tall, pink-skinned natives of more distant lands, there was little mutual understanding. However, since all of them were guests within China's borders, courtesy demanded that differences be overlooked. In the face of much opposition from his intimates, for at present a mountain of feeling was rising against the Nipponese, he had argued one recent evening in the teahouse that some of the foreign ways were good—witness their healing of the sick! And now a foreigner, not some other, had sent this child on the long journey to the spirit world of ancestors, far beyond the reach of any physician to the body.

But was this really true? his mind protested. Perhaps something could still be done for the boy lying so quietly there before him. Lin Scholar forced himself to move forward and peer through horn-rimmed spectacles at the lad's face, smooth and unmarred by any of life's harrowing problems. A sigh issued slowly from the depths of the old man's being. No, he told himself with bleak finality, regardless of whether or not his brain wished to accept the truth, those hidden eyes would never again flash with intelligence, nor the deft fingers shape a brush-pen into symmetrical strokes. Small Wang was dead.

To his dismay, Lin Scholar found body and mind, habitually restrained to rigid control, now betraying him in a spasm of grief. With the passing of this child, life's personal meaning faded for himself. Age was close upon him, and no one of his own blood remained. For six years Small Wang had been binding him with cords of affection, the ends of which had unexpectedly frayed. In the future he would have to draw ever more heavily on Ancient Wisdom to dull this aching emptiness of mind and heart and, he was suddenly reminded, that of his stomach as well. Wang Merchant was not likely to waste book learning on daughters, and with modern government schools in each corner of the city, few homes at present wished the services of a Confucian Classicist.

Impatiently he shrugged the problem of material needs from him. What were these compared with the loss of the child? In a funereal accompaniment to his own somber thoughts, there now rose from the women's courts the shrill response of a household stricken by unbelievable disaster. For a little time the machinery of normal living ceased whirring, then in an exaggerated pretense of urgency, resumed activity—man's fearful but futile gesture to demand again for Life the throne where Death already sat in full possession. Listening, Lin Scholar turned away, then moved blindly through dim, gray corridors into the heartless sunlight of the spring.

GIFT TO THE CHINESE AIR FORCE

SCENE II

When they brought the news of his only son's death to him, Wang Merchant sat in an office of the city's largest silk establishment, considering figures on the latest statement of trade. These had been increasingly good since New Year's and what the captain from the airdrome had told him only an hour ago was true; namely, that he was one of the few business men in this city who could present the government with a military airplane and not suffer financial stringency from the gift.

Wang Merchant smiled to himself. From the beginnings of time officials had been accustomed to telling ordinary citizens how to spend personal income; he himself had reached his present affluence only by being able to think faster through the years than government representatives. Indeed, half of his time and energy was absorbed in the problem of holding on to what had been so laboriously earned, and now to expect him to throw the savings of a year—well, at least those of several moons—into a flying machine that could be destroyed in a few minutes, was of a certainty absurd.

He had to admit, however, that the aviator's arguments were more sincere than those of most such solicitors. The present government was, truly enough, improving living conditions at a remarkable rate, and the country was becoming unified as never before in the Middle Kingdom's history.

To all of these assertions he had agreed, and not until the younger man began talking of the imminence of war had he expressed an opposing opinion. "Fear is a club to use on men who cannot think for themselves!" he had chided. "Six months ago the mention of Japanese aggression might have squeezed my stomach, but not now. At present their own people stir up trouble and, as a result, China breathes more freely than for several years past."

"It will be a short breath, Honorable Merchant, unless we prepare for future attack! Think a little! Is it likely their militarists will not use these internal problems to advantage? War gives work to all men, and where will Japan fight except on Chinese soil?"

"But the many birthday planes to the Generalissimo—what of them?"

"Not enough! We need ten times as many, and men properly trained to use them!"

For another fifteen minutes by the clock, Wang Merchant listened; then with a final word, "When the short-legged ones reopen their quarrel, come to me again!" he had dismissed the earnest young officer from his presence.

But not from his mind, for the arguments recurred to annoy him as he turned the account sheets! Could it be possible that further invasion was really close at hand or was the captain simply another alarmist poking in every dung heap for the seeds of calamity? After a time he slid the sheets together and clapped his hands sharply for the chief accountant.

For a moment no one answered his signal. Then the manager, himself, came slowly through the doorway. "Where is the accountant?" Wang Merchant asked but without waiting for an answer, went on, "Trade has been very good, is it not so?" Noting the other's unusually grave manner, he paused suddenly to ask, "What is the matter?"

The manager moistened his lips. "Two from your home have just arrived. They say that your son——" he sighed in difficulty, "the messengers wait now in the shop. Will you receive them here?"

Puzzled, the listener brushed aside these broken fragments of speech and demanded, "My son—what of him?"

"Friends have we been for years, Head of this Establishment, and to bring you such word is my own bitter fortune. Your son, so it is said, wandered across the Japanese boundary line this morning and was shot by a soldier. The child lies now in your home."

Blood, coursing over Wang Merchant's body, flooded head and neck and ebbed slowly again to pallor. As if questioning the reality of this preposterous statement, he stared for one endless moment into the manager's face, then without a word strode through the building into the street and, with a terse command to his personal ricksha runner waiting on the curb, was gone.

Shortly afterwards, entrance into his dwelling supplied him on every side with the confirmation of that which he still refused to believe. Already priests moved about the rooms, and tiring women prepared fillets and garments of white mourning cloth. Priests and mourners! What, he demanded savagely of the Universe, were such as these doing under this roof? At his swift approach the occupants of the room in which his son lay fell back into the shadows and their wailing voices lowered.

Aware of nothing save the slender figure stretched out before his eyes—the father, still numb to loss, stood in wonder that any creature customarily so lithe and agile should have reached this present immobility. Gradually as his gaze absorbed afresh the familiar lines and features of the dead child, his personal relationship to the other began to assume normal proportions. This was his son, he told himself dully, not some other, who lay here in death—his son on whom had been centered all of his love and all of the hopes for the future of this house. As the fact repeated itself over and over in his brain, he turned away at last and sought the quiet refuge of his own apartments.

There he sank heavily into a seat before a table and gazed with unseeing eyes at folded hands. Slowly anger rose in him, submerging grief. Why was he, with his established position in this city, sitting weak and helpless as any woman in sorrow's grip, while his son's murder remained unavenged? With a brusque command to the manservant waiting outside his door, he began to set the wheels of financial and political power into motion. Through the long hours of that afternoon, men hurried about the city on these errands, only to return to the Wang household with word of failure. In this particular case silver was proving itself an unsatisfactory weapon with which to prod officialdom into action, for the government, hesitating to offend an important merchant, feared still more to arouse ire in this national enemy that turned the simplest acts into pretexts for unlimited aggression. Citizens had been duly warned about crossing that strip of territory which Japan claimed for her own and those who did so, whether young or old, must suffer the consequences of the act.

When they brought Wang Merchant this ultimatum, he sat coldly still. There had been no need for a war to cause desolation under his own roof; without extra effort the Japanese, working silently and efficiently here in his own city, had brought that to pass. And if the government dared risk no further "incident" for these devils to seize upon, then he, himself, must think up some personal means of vengeance.

Meanwhile, what of those to blame here in his own household? They, at least, should suffer promptly for this—the servant who attended the boy in play; the scholar whose duty it was to keep the child busy at his books; his son's mother, *ai!* more than all others, the mother! What duty had women but to look after children? Was not the house overrun with servants to do the bidding of this woman and her seven useless daughters? One son only had she borne him, one son after a terrifying succession of girls, and now this son was gone. Who, Filial Duty inquired of him, would attend to the ancestral tablets when he himself "ascended the Dragon"? Of their direct line only a half brother remained, and that one, although he had been their dead father's favorite, was none-the-less a wastrel and a fool.

Memory prodded grief into a renewed flicking at the raw wound. In all his life two creatures only had he, the shrewd builder of a fortune, loved—his father and this boy—and today's suffering was suddenly intensified by recalling that of the past. His father, to whom he had given the richness of youth's disinterested affection, had been indifferent to the offering; the latter's eyes had been blind to all but his younger son, a child of old age and a girlish concubine. And, while the passing years had taken this parent with them and, by the ancient laws, Wang Merchant and not his brother had received the inheritance, the bitter envy in the older man's heart had not abated. For many years, tenderness had been dead within him and his energy had become ruthless in its single-minded concentration on business.

Only when his own son was born had life grown less mechanical. From infancy the boy had shown rich promise, and recently a betrothal to the daughter of an old friend, whose family record and financial standing resembled the Wangs' own, had been arranged. United by marriage, these two houses could become a power in provincial trade such as neither might hope to be alone; they would—abruptly this dream faded to a gray awakening—they would do nothing, the merchant told himself with bitter finality, for one of those betrothed was already dead.

In the first shock of grief, the inescapable fact that his younger brother was now the only heir had not presented itself to full consciousness. With recognition of this came the swift determination that were no other means to be found by which to outwit this stroke of fate, then he would wreck his fortune rather than see it fall in the other's eager hands. Harsh laughter rose suddenly to his lips. Awaiting only his decision to employ it, lay the perfect tool for accomplishing this end. With a word or two he could decrease appreciably the silver stored to his credit and at the same time purchase weapons of destruction to be used against Japan. The young captain should have not one military airplane, but several, and little time should be lost in notifying the aviation department of this fact.

As for his own future and his duty to the ancestral tablets, the problem remained unchanged. In this respect, or in any other for that matter, the younger brother could be counted upon for nothing at all. That his own wife would bear him another son at her age was beyond possibility, and he would have to consider taking a concubine. Although women had never held special interest for him, as soon as propriety permitted, a go-between should be consulted about this matter. His own body was still virile and he would specify that the woman be young and strong for breeding purposes. If she gave him one son to carry on his name and life work, he would be satisfied.

Abruptly despair seized him. That one or many sons would be able to lift his heart from this present abyss of grief was beyond hope. Two creatures had he loved—in youth, his father who had not cared and had died; in maturity, an agile, bright-eyed boy who had returned the affection, but had died just the same. In a gesture of defeat, Wang Merchant's head sank wearily to rest on folded arms.

Scene III

Leaning against the beautifully carved back rail of his bed, Wang, the Younger, lifted a tea bowl from the small table beside him and noted the quivering muscles in his extended arm. More sleep was his great need, he told himself, as he gulped the steaming draught—for even though the time was almost midday, the game last night had, as usual, lasted until the Hour of the Tiger, and he had arrived home only when the household was beginning to stir for the day's work.

A tempting morsel of food found its way to his mouth, then was spat out irritably on the tiled floor. Lately breakfasts tasted as if they were mixed with poison, and perhaps they were—certainly that miser, his elder brother, would be glad to see him gone! Ever since their father had "ascended the Dragon," Life had woven for him, the younger son, a pattern of increasingly evil threads, he told himself from the depths of self-pity. Throughout youth he had been refused nothing, and now a load-bearer could hardly be expected to live on that pittance which his guardian, the silk merchant, so flatteringly called a generous allowance. The money did not even pay for his clothes; certainly it took into account none of those interesting pursuits in which every young man of fashion indulged.

He rose slowly and slipped soiled, satin garments over the thin, white silk ones that already robed him. This mulberry brocade was not wearing so well as might have been expected from the price paid for it. Perhaps he ought to send the tailor for material next time to that new shop of which everyone was talking. He yawned, wondering idly if there would be any difficulty about getting credit there, for his affairs were certainly in a bad way.

How to improve them was the problem. His elder brother reminded him all too frequently that most men worked in order to spend—a suggestion that fell on deaf ears, so far as the unwilling listener was concerned. Instead, all of his hopes had centered on the dominoes, and for the past ten days he had experienced losses and no gains. If memory had not failed him at the wrong moment, there was one play possible last night that might have changed the tide. Perhaps this evening another such opportunity would present itself. No! The idea was dismissed with a frown—tonight his boon companions could find another fowl to pluck.

He grasped his head in both hands. A little opium would quiet that pain, but it would also make him even sleepier than now, and he had to think clearly and find some solution for his difficulties. Moreover, if his brain had not been dulled by the drug two nights earlier, he would never have become so involved in the affair with the girl at the teahouse. Something had to be done about that even if the rest of his obligations had to wait. Why he had asked the old woman to hold her for his special entertainment and services was unfathomable here in broad daylight. There were hundreds of more desirable girls in this city and now, by a single foolish request, the entire support of this one had fallen on his shoulders.

A hurried knocking on the door distracted him from these unpleasant considerations. "Come!" he ordered.

In response his personal servant entered and broke at once into excited speech. Within the next few moments, in possession of the fact that his only nephew lay dead a few rooms away, the young man's emotions shifted exultingly from despair to elation, although his countenance, under the servant's scrutinizing gaze, held to its first hastily assumed expression of horror-stricken grief. Not until the man had been dismissed did Wang, the Younger, permit his features to relax.

With the son and heir of this house out of the way he, and no one else, was the next in line of succession to the entire family fortune, he told himself over and over as he strode about the room. This meant an end to all financial problems. That only a moment since he had worried about obtaining further credit now seemed absurdly amusing. On the strength of an undivided inheritance coming to him at Wang, the Elder's, death, shopkeepers and usurers would advance him unlimited amounts. First, the girl must be paid for; then a complete new wardrobe should receive his attention. As for the game—winning would now become a certainty; losers were always those whose pockets were empty of coin.

His lips pursed together thoughtfully. For a period, and that perhaps a lengthy one, there would be no roistering for anyone under this roof, where Death was now in command. Well, he could wait, and meanwhile no one should mourn more diligently than he! After all, though he had thought of the boy as an immovable obstacle in his path, polite relations had always been observed, and for the uncle to wear an attitude of grief along with the sorrowful habiliments that custom entailed, would seem natural enough to the casual spectator.

In spite of these temporary unpleasantnesses, the fact remained that he was the heir—the direct heir—to his brother's entire fortune. *Ai-ya,* but the Wheel of Life sometimes spun to queer stops! Wang, the Younger, stood and sucked the sweetness from this moment of realization, then changing to neater garments, he drew a veil of soberness over his features, and crossed the house to pay immediate respects to the dead.

Scene IV

Beside the "Pool of Many Shadows" in her garden, Wang Mistress sat on a low stone seat and studied her folded hands. It seemed strange she thought, holding her straying attention captive for a moment, that one who had never known idleness should now deliberately drop so many unused hours into Time's scavenging basket. In the house partially finished pieces of embroidery and knitting had lain for weeks awaiting her creative touch and there they would continue, for today, when living itself seemed no longer worth the effort required to do so, she felt surprised that there could ever have been a purpose in starting such unimportant tasks.

Without interest her gaze wandered upward between branches of a willow, twisted and gnarled by age. At the top, precariously perched, was a large, slovenly nest where magpies came and went their insolent ways. An old bird now lighted on one of the lower limbs and poised half-balanced to scold raucously about this human presence at the pool. Something about its angle of cocked head and sparkling eye brought Wang Mistress a fresh reminder of her son. He had a similar gesture of keen attention, as though he were leaning to catch whispered advice from the Spirit of Mischief itself, before darting into further activity. His eyes, his eyes—she sucked in a dry, painful breath—*Kuan-yin!* was it possible he had been gone more than a moon—a moon since they had brought him home, still and lifeless, after that brief half hour of play?

When they told her, she had been embroidering shoes for herself, delicately beautiful coverings for those stubs of deformity and suffering which men, through the centuries, had been pleased to call "Golden Lilies." An ironic shadow flitted over her face. And women, herself among them, fiercely refusing to acknowledge the bondage that crippled feet forced upon their lives, had through those same centuries kept up the pretense of pride in their possession. Heaven be praised—that custom was at last changing! Her three youngest girls walked naturally and while this fact had made the matter of betrothals with sons of conservative houses a little more difficult for them than for their older sisters, it also gave them a freedom of movement that the others would never know. Watching them, she wondered frequently how it must feel to stretch from heel to toe those muscles which in her own feet were but a hard, numbed knot of tortured flesh.

That the promised daughter-in-law also walked freely was a satisfaction. *Ai!* Her thoughts clouded with weary exasperation. Why did memory trick her into moments of forgetting that her son was gone, and that no daughter-in-law would ever enter this house to serve her as she herself had once served others? Forty-nine years had she lived and not yet could she recall those early days of her own marriage without flesh crawling on her spine. Strangely enough her misery had not been of a mother-in-law's devising, for that one had been old and kind, much too gentle to fight for her rightful position under a roof where a spoiled concubine clutched greedily at every source of power. What a devil for cruelty this favorite had been, Wang Mistress knew better than most, for she, the young bride, without a single friend in the household, save her helpless mother-in-law, had been completely at the other woman's mercy.

Once, thinking herself unable to endure another day of such existence, she had appealed to her husband, but no help had been forthcoming. He had never loved her, and even today the wound that his refusal had made in her pride remained unhealed. Only when his father had followed his mother in death, had he acted. The concubine had then been given her own wing of the house and a generous income, but she had been shorn of power, and shortly afterwards spleen from frustration added to self-indulgence had killed her.

In his way her husband was a just man, Wang Mistress admitted fairly. During those years when she had borne him one daughter after the other, he had never threatened her with a second wife. Then, at last, a son had come and with his birth had placed her in that position of security and happiness that all women craved. The reality of the gift had been almost beyond belief to one who had waited through what seemed an eternity for its arrival and, as a result, she had trodden her days with soft and quiet step, faithfully observing every duty to the ancestors and giving frequent choice offerings to Kuan-yin in the temple near-by. Twice during the years she had made trying pilgrimages to the sacred mountain, but Heaven, it seemed, had been blind to these oblations and had taken her son just the same.

With bitter repetition, she curled her tongue around the old proverb, "Whether a child be born early or late is unimportant; what is to be feared is that Fate will give it short life."

Truly! Her own son had not only been born late, but his life had been abruptly shortened as well. Boy though he was, he had carried away with him that flood of color and sunlight which his presence had added to the gray, unchanging pattern of her days. Her mind studied this personal fabric of existence in swift appraisal of the feelings and emotions that had been its most stoutly woven threads. The relationships with her own family had been almost completely severed, and the love so timidly offered her husband in those early years had shredded to a few weak fibers long ago. As for her daughters—like that of most Chinese mothers, her affection for them had always been a delicate skein strained by the certainty of future partings. Was it possible, she asked herself thoughtfully, that an occasional faded design of friendship and the toughly resistant threads of duty, which were all that remained to hold warp and woof together, warranted mending of the whole against the future's inescapable wear and tear? Already her husband had told her that, having no direct heir but his worthless half brother, he felt it necessary to bring another woman into the house, and the matter would soon be arranged. With her son dead and her daughters soon gone to their new homes, what place or need remained for her, the first wife, in this house?

Pondering this question she stared with unseeing eyes into a morning from which the sun had disappeared. A chilling wind now touched the patient face under sleek, black hair and at the same time ruffled the feathers of a magpie on a branch overhead. As the bird shifted position, a sparkling pebble, fascinating trophy for the nest, dropped from the predacious claws and plunged into the water below. Startled by the splash of falling stone, Wang Mistress turned, then in the sudden grip of purposeful thought she began to reflect intently on this slight accident which had left behind no disturbing trace of its occurrence except a series of ever-widening circles on the green, translucent surface of the pool.

Scene V

The commander of the local airdrome eyed the discouraged expression on his youngest captain's face that late spring afternoon and commented with a quizzical smile, "So, our merchants do not untie their moneybags easily, is it not true?"

For a second the junior officer's shoulders sagged, then straightened again to military attention. "Daily in the past moon have I gone from north to south and east to west in this district asking help for the Air Force; daily the same record has been written. Those who have little silver share freely; those who possess much hold it tight in their fists. Ten men there are in the city alone who could give us a machine; no one of them will do so. 'I must educate many in my family!' or 'My son is to marry before the Period of

Early Heat!' or 'My mother's funeral was the most expensive in the history of this section!' they tell me, one after another, until their excuses make my stomach hurt."

"And you say what to them?"

"Sir, my tongue is thick from shaping words about better air defenses. I talk of need for planes and for trained men to fly them, until no saliva is left in my cheeks. Then, when I have finished, these fat, comfortable merchants tell me to wait until Japan attacks. 'When the short-legged ones reopen their quarrel, come to me again!' Wang, the silk merchant, advised. *Ai-ya!* that one could pay for two machines and his piles of silver would still look like small mountains." He drew a long breath of weariness. "Perhaps, I need a begging-bowl and rags to win their interest!"

His companion threw him an understanding glance. "You and I are flyers, and to ask others to part with their silver is bitter work for us. However, we must have planes." A strange light flickered for an instant in his eyes. "Suppose Wang gave us five ships—what then?"

"Japan, Sir, would be as likely to do so," the captain retorted wryly; "though even so Wang's family would not starve, I believe."

"Let us hope not! Read this!" The commander pushed a letter across the table and awaited his subordinate's reaction with interest.

When the other again looked up, his expression was set in amazement. "So it was the silk merchant's child, and not another's, that sentry shot!"

"That one's, indeed, and the only son of the house!"

"His only son—*ai!*" For a moment there was silence, then the captain resumed wonderingly, "And for vengeance the dead child's father gives us bombers to use on the enemy. Not one or two, but five—it may be his family *will* starve!"

"Not for food, where silver is so ready to the hand; what grief may do to them, Heaven alone can say." He paused lost in thought, then added slowly, "Strange, it is, that we owe thanks to Japan for these machines! Of a certainty, the God of War must be amused."

Later, outside, the captain halted and gazed upward to that vast expanse of blue which was his own special field of action. Five bombers! He wondered if the models would be American or Italian and whether he would have the privilege of testing these ships which occupied so peculiar a place in his mind, paid for, as they had been, by the unusual coin of a murdered child's life. Ironically Japan had, on this occasion, exceeded her aim. With a grimly expressive smile twisting his lips, the aviator faced in the direction of the disputed strip of territory. "This time, Nippon," he exclaimed aloud, "you 'threw at the rat and broke the vase!'" Turning, he walked slowly toward his own quarters for the night.

臨患難當思人亦如是 時諺

THE WOMAN

In unhappiness think of others who grieve also!

One of the most remarkable facts in China's history is that there should have been so many self-sacrificing mothers in a land which demanded of its womanhood, and still does though to a lesser degree, an abnegation during youth and middle age of individual desire and purpose almost inconceivable to Western minds, and which in age placed in those same feminine hands unlimited opportunity for personal indulgence and tyranny over others. In the annals of the human race, there are few instances of men and women who, even when accustomed to power from birth, have failed to succumb to the insidious temptation of using it unjustly. And yet through the long centuries, there has been worked into the Chinese pattern of civilization the rather startling idea that, after forty years or more of accepting without question the rules laid down for her by others, a woman is then fitted to assume in turn the management of all younger lives within her household.

It would seem that only the ingrained teaching of *Li*, perhaps the most important word in the Chinese language, with its intensive concentration on the "Five Virtues"—knowledge, integrity, self-respect, propriety, and kindliness—and the "Five Relationships"—emperor and subject, parent and child, husband and wife, older brother and younger brother, friend and friend—made this system function with any degree of success. Where all of the members of a family dwelt under one common roof, it was so difficult for men, assisted though they were by outside contacts of work and recreation, to live without friction that one of China's wisest patriarchs, when asked the secret of his own harmonious family circle, wrote in answer a single ideograph, over and over—the word, "Forbearance." As for the women, most of whom possessed in full measure the racial characteristics of initiative and ingenuity, the petty restrictions and limitations of their lives in the confines of their courts must have presented a problem which unceasing mental and spiritual discipline alone could have controlled.

To the average Chinese household the birth of a daughter, however welcome she might be, caused little excitement; for, from the moment of her arrival in the world, she occupied much the same position as a guest in her family, destined after due time to leave for a permanent residence with her husband's people. From a legal, and frequently a social, standpoint she was lost to her own home on the day of her marriage as completely as if she had been removed from its sheltering walls by death.

臨患難當思人亦如是
時諺

臨患難當思人亦如是
時諺

In the new establishment which absorbed her, the bride experienced little change in position. For father-in-law and mother-in-law, she was expected to perform services similar to those she had formerly rendered her own parents. Her status improved as she gave birth to children, with a special emphasis in the case of sons, but even then it was unlikely that she would be permitted any great amount of freedom in the rearing of her offspring. Had not Good Fortune provided her husband's wise and experienced mother for this very purpose of dictating all that pertained to food, clothing, training, and play for these new lives?

If the young mother felt her heart go out to a small daughter, the emotion must, of necessity, have been tempered by the ever-present shadow of certain separation a little later. Cold wisdom reminded her that in her sons lay all hope of permanence in relationship, for with one of them, probably the eldest, she would end her days. What was of equal importance was that his marriage would insure for her possession of service and attention identical with that which through youth and middle age irked her own mind and heart so greatly in the giving.

Naturally enough occasional tragedies occurred as a result of this system, but in spite of temptation to do otherwise, a wholesome proportion of mothers-in-law and daughters-in-law managed to adjust themselves happily to each other, and unsung millions of mothers gave their sons and daughters as wholehearted and disinterested a devotion as if the future and its risks did not exist. In tribute to this capacity for selflessness, the Chinese people for almost twenty-three hundred years have paid honor to a woman who represents the ideal maternal figure of the race—Chang-hsi, the mother of Mencius. An impoverished widow with a small son to rear, she resorted to weaving, one of the very few ways in which a Chinese woman of the fourth century B.C. could earn income. Her struggles to eke out existence and at the same time train her son to be worthy of a virtuous and scholarly ancestry offer an inspiring example of womanhood regardless of race. In *The Importance of Living*, Lin Yu-tang says, "The success of widows in giving their children a perfect education of character and morals has often led me to think that fathers are totally unnecessary, so far as the *upbringing* of children is concerned."

In China, except with the very poor, a child knows two mothers, since weaning rarely occurs until the baby is three years old. Naturally this custom drains the real mother's strength and also postpones further childbearing, her chief duty in life. To avoid these difficulties a wet nurse is hired to feed the infant, and

臨患難當思人亦如是
時諺

臨患難當思人亦如是
時諺

Chinese generally refer to these "milk mothers" in terms of cordial appreciation. Also, where foreign children have been cared for by Chinese amahs, there have been forged bonds of affection that have lasted through the years.

But if Chinese women have excelled as wives and mothers, they have shown other remarkable capacities as well. For many centuries a woman's opportunities were limited to the domestic scene or, in rare cases, to the court. There are a number of examples where an empress or a regent exercised great power and in several instances instituted unusual reforms in government. Favorites, in particular, wielded influence, and their policies ranged from the nationally ruinous program of the irresistible Yang Kuei-fei to that of lovely Wang Chao-chun, who accepted a living death rather than embroil her country in further warfare.

In the past hundred years China's women, like most others in the world, have been given their opportunity to forge ahead, and at present there remain few professional or business fields in which they have not achieved outstanding success. Today, in the defense against Japanese invaders, China's women are everywhere active as physicians and nurses to the wounded, teachers in refugee camps, workers on farms and in factories, and some have even caught up soldiers' falling weapons and filled the gaps in the trenches. Beside the Generalissimo, himself, encouraging, guiding, strengthening him through her own faith and courage, stands Madame Chiang Kai-shih, typical of her race's womanhood in greatness of spirit.

Although lowly in rank, the amah in *Under the Skin* is as representative as the "First Lady." Regardless of Fortune's favors or the lack of them in life, Chinese women leave the imprint of grace and beauty, courage and patience, on their days. Among young and old, courtesy and hospitality flower as readily in meager, poverty-stricken surroundings as in the courtyards of the wealthy, and kindliness to one in need is no more the attribute of the official's lady than of the coolie-woman in the fields.

臨患難當思人亦如是

時諺

臨患難當思人亦如是

時諺

霍林路

UNDER THE SKIN

Mrs. Shelton, standing patiently in the jam that waited at the press dispatch office for news from the Northern Front, noticed that the same coolie-woman who had pressed her in the two days past was again exhaling a far-from-pleasant breath of pungent foods, as she maneuvered into position immediately behind. With resentment the foreigner gave the blue-clad native a deliberate frown of repugnance and then, for a fleeting second, watched its effect.

The round, placid face revealed no trace of affront. Its owner, avoiding the foreigner's eyes by a tiny fraction of space, continued unblinkingly to direct her own gaze on the queue of people ahead. A small, toilworn hand lifted to her mouth and with a forefinger and thumb pried loose a fragment of food from between two molars. Then, as though satisfied with the success of this achievement, an audible belch punctuated the action, the arm slipped again downward, and Mrs. Shelton faced hastily about.

How impossible they were—these uncouth natives! She experienced a faint nausea as she recalled this and similar crudities that she had been forced to meet since her arrival in Shanghai. What under heaven did Carl see in them? And why had she been so foolish as to let him persuade her that she, too, might respond to the same lodestone of attraction as had drawn him for the past five years? In her own heart she had sensed clearly the fact that fifty-five was not likely to be swept off its feet by sensations which youth described in phrases of adventure and romance only. Such hypnotic terminology had caught her son in the highly suggestible middle twenties, and he had not yet recovered. There was, however, no excuse for her own weakness in having agreed to come here for a six months' stay—no reason at all, save injured vanity and the desire to prolong this period of renewed companionship with him. She smiled ruefully to herself. Since they were now separated by hundreds of miles, the companionship counted for little, and if vanity had to bear the brunt of her present state of mind, it was a costly emotion, indeed!

Instead of standing here between this objectionable woman and a portly Chinese gentleman whose two smallest fingers wore nails two inches long, she might now be in her own pleasant apartment in Baltimore, thousands of miles away from Shanghai's indescribable clamors and odors. For no matter how much Carl talked of improved living conditions in this port city, one had merely to step off the main thoroughfares to be engulfed in waves of filth and squalor.

Longing for the familiar swept over her—black Nancy, who for twenty years had moved capably about lifting from her mistress' shoulders all responsibility for the mechanics of living; Edward and Elinor running in and out with the babies; her old and tried friends, the new Art Museum, the occasional visit of the Philharmonic Orchestra, and her clubs. Together these had filled her life acceptably until Carl's disturbing furlough.

He had been little more than adolescent when he first sailed in 1925 to fill his berth with an import-export firm; he had returned a man, mature and searching in his judgments. After a month or so of natural readjustments, he had turned to her one evening at the close of dinner, and said slowly, "Mother, you look as youthful as when I went away, but you seem much older."

Surprised, she had set down the silver coffeepot hastily, splashing a drop on a saucer of the delicate rice-patterned porcelain he had brought her as a gift, and replied, "Five years are five years!"

"Five years!" Carl had reached for his cup. "More than five are needed to explain the difference in you. Perhaps you are too comfortable. Yes, of course, you know some solicitude for Ned's affairs and mine," he had nodded as she attempted a futile protest, "but otherwise you have no cares." He hesitated a moment, weighing words, "As a result you are nothing like so stimulating mentally as you were in those days when you wondered how you would ever stretch your income, and your energy as well, over the demands that Ned and I made on them. You need fresh interests."

To cover her smarting reaction, she had absorbed the offending drop of coffee on the edge of one of her best napkins. For the time words were beyond her grasp, and Carl's voice, broken by the puff of a cigarette, had continued, "Out there—I wish you could see it—foreigners—Americans and Europeans—at each other's throat in competitive trade; natives fighting with every ounce of energy in them simply to last from the cradle to the grave! Even I have been wrecked in the Yangtze Gorges, shot at by bandits, caught in a plague-infested village—experiences that sound frightful to American ears, but in that stage setting are only everyday life." He paused and then went on. "Except for that one short trip to Europe years ago, you have not been off this continent. Be a good sport and go back with me for six months, at least. I want the fun of sharing your response to that land which is likely to be my home throughout the future. You need not indulge in bandits or wrecks—I'll see to that," he promised with a smile.

In the end when she could forget the first sting of his criticism, she had made up her mind suddenly to accompany him. The thought of his sailing away from her again to a land whose name had become a synonym for trouble and excitement was more than she could bear. Perhaps she *was* growing too fond of ease and her own settled way of living. Such a journey would, as Carl believed, doubtless furnish her with fresh interests. Certainly, the preparation had touched her spirit with a zest she had not felt in years!

How rapidly this had faded! Of course, even Carl could not have foreseen that China would welcome them on arrival with a war. He had been so eager to step on the mud flats of Shanghai once more that he had paid little attention to her enthusiasm over picturesque Japan. The courtesy and apparent friendliness of the island shopkeepers had been for her the most charming part of the trip. And China, as represented by Shanghai—which Carl insisted was only a fringe of the real country's garment—had disappointed her more than she dared to say. There was little in these less colorful people to which her own spirit answered. They wore what Ned would call a "poker face," and service was not so flashily embroidered with smiles and lilting phrases.

When she mentioned this, her son, who had few words of praise for Nippon, had replied with the irritation of a man whose pet theory is criticized adversely. "Do you permit strangers to break down your reserve immediately? No more do the Chinese. Just give them time, Mother, and you will discover any number of qualities to attract you."

So far no time had been given her to study them through Carl's sympathetic eyes. One week after landing, he had left on an emergency call to the firm's offices in Tientsin and Peiping and the train on which he was scheduled to return had been derailed in the North China fighting area. His office had told her that Carl was in no real danger; such things happened often with few resultant casualties. He was simply detained and in a few days would be back in Shanghai, laughing over this new play in the game of living in the Orient. To still her own instinctive fear she had accepted the opiate of their confidence in his well-being and doled it out as her spirit demanded. Activity was what she needed, but there was none, save this daily appearance at the news building. She had not mentioned it to the people at the office. They would have insisted on doing the errand for her, or suggested using the telephone, and neither of these would have given her real satisfaction. Only by experiencing this unpleasant ordeal in person could she succeed in annihilating any of the distance between her son and herself. In the whirring pressrooms a flood of dispatches poured in from the battle lines, and there was always a possibility of some more definite word about the wrecked train.

Six people were still ahead of her. A handsome Sikh policeman wearing a red turban—the only bright spot in a sea of blue, black, and brown—was now receiving attention. A Frenchman tapped a walking stick impatiently near the Sikh's heels. One huge, bearded Russian, three Chinese, then herself—how slowly they moved! She had slept little since the word came, and this morning her head throbbed. Shifting weight wearily from one foot to the other, she glanced again at the coolie-woman. If Carl were here, he would tell her, no doubt, that this woman was not coolie class—he made so many distinctions. But the fact that the same fingers which only a short time ago had extracted food from teeth were now digging into a scalp where coarse, black hair strained back from a yellow forehead was evidence enough of the creature's social status.

Mrs. Shelton drew her slender body forward tautly in an effort to escape further contact. She had always been fastidious about touch, and all of her distaste for these people, all of her fear for Carl's safety, merged into feeling against this individual woman. With relief she watched the gentleman of long fingernails step out of line. Moving forward she asked the Eurasian clerk, "Can you tell me if there has been further word of the derailed train?"

He nodded, then in staccato syllables read a wire: "Chinese crew killed. Unidentified American seriously injured. May be C. J. Shelton, Harwood Company, Shanghai."

Mrs. Shelton stood where she was. Seriously injured! Carl—her baby—Carl! But they had said he couldn't be hurt; he would be back in a few days laughing over the adventure. Carl! Dear God! what did one do in moments like this in a strange land?

Words were being exchanged behind her, and a long, sibilant breath whistling in her ear startled her back to consciousness of surroundings. Dazed, she turned to find the native woman focusing a look of naked fear into space. Aware instantly of the foreigner's eyes, the black ones slowly resumed their usual expressionless mask. Human fragments from the dissolving line now flowed past these two figures. Mrs. Shelton stepped from their path and found herself on a bench. She must stop her body's foolish shaking before going to the office. Even the expensive, black suede bag on her lap was trembling under the tight clutch of her cold fingers. Carl had admired the hand-carved silver mounting, but had told her it did not compare with Chinese work in that metal. When he had a chance, he would get her a piece from Foochow.

When he had a chance! Where was he now? Seriously injured carried the double meaning of death. The wire had used the words, "unidentified and may be." Perhaps there had been a mistake. Perhaps—no, she told herself dully, it was her son, not another. There was no sense in deluding her reason with false hope. She would go to the office; they would have to get some more definite word at once. If only there were someone she loved and trusted, to whom she might turn in this hour! The few friends Carl had asked to watch out for her in his absence had all been cordial enough, but they were his contemporaries, not hers.

She could not share grief with those gay, young things. Her shivering body responded slowly to control. It was as Carl had said—life had made her soft.

She rose and moved uncertainly on wobbling knees toward the exit. A small, firm hand reached out to steady her and a soft voice whispered in halting speech, "Missee sick—catchee licsaw, go home!"

The speaker was the coolie-woman. Mrs. Shelton smothered her first impulse to pull away, and before her distracted brain could further consider refusing this unexpected aid, she found her body relying treacherously on the other's strength. In another moment they were on the sidewalk and the round face was hallooing for a ricksha. When the vehicle appeared, the woman helped her into it and asked directions for the runner. Mrs. Shelton hesitated. In her present state she could not face a businesslike office. But to go home to Carl's empty house and meet his imperturbable Number-one Boy, of whom she was still half afraid, would be equally difficult. She never understood fully what prompted her next decision. With quivering lips she turned to the native woman, "Can call other ricksha; go with me, please!"

At the house, the servant glanced once at her white face and then without further ado paid the coolies, ushered his master's mother and her strange companion into the reception room, then repeated a telephone call to the effect that the office was sending up a telegram by special messenger.

Mrs. Shelton motioned her native guest to a seat, sank down on the nearest sofa, and with clumsy fingers removed the hat from her throbbing head. A telegram by special messenger! This would be confirmation of her worst fears. They would have telephoned directly any less important word. She was trapped—she wanted to scream, to rush from the room—anything, rather than to sit here and receive the blow while these wretched strangers looked curiously on. She had been out of her mind to bring this woman to the house. She must tell the servant to give her some money and send her away now—at once.

But the Number-one Boy and the woman were chattering in their own outlandish tongue. Carl had planned to teach her some of the simpler phrases. He had said—God in heaven! Carl might, Carl *would* never say anything again. It couldn't be true! Perhaps she was coming out of ether once more and this horrible nightmare belonged with others in that limbo of indescribable tortures.

The servant's voice brushed her thoughts: "This woman say Missee catchee bad news. Missee sick; all better go bed sleep. She help Missee bed, then chop-chop go workee amah-work foreign house."

A ringing bell interrupted and the boy slipped from the room.

With gravity the amah eyed the American woman, clicked her tongue sympathetically, then turned attention to a gnarled shrub that grew from a jade-green jar. "Plitty!" she murmured under her breath.

Mrs. Shelton, her ears straining for the messenger's footsteps, caught the remark and lifted agonized eyes. The irony of being forced to listen at this moment while a stranger admired flowers! How like this impassive race to remain undisturbed by another's suffering!

The door opened and Carl's Chinese manager entered. After a courteous greeting, he told her the office had just received a message from Mr. Shelton. Aware of her anxiety, they had decided to place the telegram in her hands instead of telephoning its contents, and he had permitted himself the pleasure of bringing this good news. Mr. Shelton was unharmed and would return to Shanghai shortly by steamer. No lives had been lost, and only two were slightly injured—both of these Chinese. It was as they had told her: accidents of this sort happened, but foreigners rarely suffered harm.

His last sentence was lost on her ears. She grasped the typewritten slip of paper and read it avidly over and over. Her throat was opening and closing convulsively and a stinging moisture burned her eyelids. The shock of relief was more than she could bear.

When she regained composure, it was to accept a glass of cold water from the servant's hands. The amah's interest concentrated on the shrub. The manager's back was discreetly turned to her; he looked through a long French window into the garden. How thoughtful! Of course, this man with his fluent English and gracious manner was of the better class, but even the houseboy had sensed her need of a drink.

The manager now approached her and bowed his farewell. He would send more definite word about the steamer as soon as he could was his promise. With curious intentness the amah watched him depart. Then as the servant re-entered the room, she, too, rose to go.

Mrs. Shelton reached for the black suede bag and thought how much more attractive this woman was when she smiled. She took one silver dollar from the enclosed purse and held it out.

The amah made no move to accept, and the servant intervened, "She no savvy."

"I wish to give her something for her kindness."

There was a rapid fire of Chinese. "She say she no wanchee money. She wanchee ask Missee—she think maybe too much tlouble—she——"

"I don't quite understand."

"She wanchee know teleglam say guards on train killed."

"Guards? No one was killed." Mrs. Shelton caught up the slip of paper. "Two people were slightly injured. But

—does she know these guards?" One terrified look in the news office now beat on her memory.

"She say her son guard on train. Paper-man tell her guards all killed."

Understanding surged over the American in a painful flood. This woman had all of the time been suffering as she, herself, had suffered until the wire came. And she, Anne Shelton, had thought the other impassive. With staining cheeks she remembered adjectives less choice that she had used to describe the amah to herself. Blind and petty in her judgments—certainly this incident was proving Carl's theories one after the other.

The despised, blue-clad form stood considering seriously the reprieve contained in the servant's last remark to her. Mrs. Shelton rose suddenly to the moment. "Telephone the office her son's name and tell them to spare no expense in finding out whether he was one of the injured people. Then serve tea here for two. Use the leaves your master keeps for his special guests. I shall write a note to this amah's mistress explaining her delay, and when she has finished tea, you will call a ricksha for her."

The boy disappeared and, suiting her vocabulary to a meager pidgin-English, she repeated the gist of this for the amah's benefit. A half-dozen Chinese phrases from the other were followed by a frowning attempt to capture English words of appreciation. With a smile Mrs. Shelton acknowledged this effort, then moving to a desk, reached for paper and pen, and threw her guest, once more perched on the edge of a chair seat, a slight glance of apology for this seeming discourtesy.

The black eyes, now luminous with gratitude, met her own in passing and held them fixed in a strange bond of feeling. With a deep indrawing of breath the American woman, at last, broke the spell. Slowly she picked up her pen and began to write.

THE ARTISAN

速則不達
孔子

The best results are won by working slowly.

If any one Chinese virtue occurs more widely and to more marked degree than others, it is probably integrity in workmanship. For regardless of task classification or the social strata on which it may be performed, the ultimate aim of achievement seems to be in reaching the standard of quality which exists in the worker's mind. Whether a potter struggling to perfect a glaze; an ivory carver laboring for years on a screen worth a king's ransom; or a humble housewife stitching shoe soles for her family, the same patient and painstaking attention is given to detail, the same effort poured into producing what will not only serve the immediate purpose, but will have beauty and durability as well. Satisfaction in work well done seems to be its own reward in China; certainly no other is apparent in this land where labor, even when it becomes creative art—and only the thinnest line exists between Chinese artist and artisan—is the cheapest of all commodities.

This racial characteristic of thoroughness may be due to the Middle Kingdom's having been throughout the centuries a civilization composed of individual industrialists. The largest establishments rarely consisted of more than the proprietor and six or seven

則不達

孔子

helpers; great factories and mills appeared only with the introduction of foreign methods. Any man trained in a craft could set up business for himself in his own home; doing all the work in person or being assisted by the members of his household until that day when he could afford to feed and shelter an apprentice. As the business justified expansion, other apprentices were added and these, in time, became full-fledged helpers.

This industrial system offered tremendous competition, and the newcomer had not only to equal, but to excel the products of other craftsmen already established in the field in order to tempt his shrewd and thrifty countrymen, conservative in matters of trade as in everything else, to switch patronage from them to him. As a result the ambitious artisan-proprietor toiled diligently to achieve the best work of which he was capable, examining each finished object meticulously before stamping his seal upon the surface and releasing it for sale.

Usually the head of such an establishment was troubled by few of the labor problems that irk the West. There were practically no laws to protect either employer or employee, but the various craft guilds substituted successfully for government supervision. With a few simple rules based on common sense, these

則不達

孔子

organizations easily settled most difficulties that were brought to their attention. Public opinion was their strongest ally, for "loss of face" acted as a powerful deterrent on antisocial activities whether they originated in proprietor or men.

The question of working hours, for instance, caused little discussion. Everyone in a shop, the owner included, labored equally long and expected to do nothing else. Pride in production and loyalty to the establishment spread contagiously from the head down to the newest apprentice and did much to eliminate discontent. The reputation for fine workmanship was attended by prosperity, in which all employees, to varying degrees, would eventually share; what was equally valuable was the prestige it gave each workman, regardless of his individual ability as a craftsman. When depressions occurred, caused usually by flood, famine, or war, the employees, realizing that they could not expect more than the owner had to give, patiently shared his ill-fortune and worked hopefully toward that day when silver would again pour into the coffers.

Two circumstances contributed particularly toward this co-operation in industry. One was the custom of having workmen and apprentices eat at the owner's table and frequently live under his roof in all the intimacy of family life. The second was to pass a

father's lifework on to his son, and he, in turn, to succeeding generations. When a youth showed unusual mental alertness, combined family efforts were made to educate him for the scholar's career; otherwise, a farmer's son from babyhood was taught cultivation of the soil; the merchant's male offspring learned, along with nursery rimes, the phrases common to bargaining; and the coppersmith's boy early became familiar with the tools of his father's craft.

Accordingly, the industrial shop, like the commercial, was often family controlled, and with expansion became a colony concentrated on one art. In time the community where it was located became known for this specialized production. Nanking, the southern capital, for example, offered a variety of articles for sale, but the experienced trader knew it as a market in which to purchase satins, velvets, and tapestries. Through the open doorways on the city's crowded streets, he could see the ubiquitous small loom kept constantly in motion by one member of a family or another—humble producers of those rich and beautiful fabrics which have attracted the covetous eyes of the world from Ancient Rome until the present day. Chinkiang, on the lower Yangtze, became famous for inlaid mother-of-pearl work; Foochow, in the south, devoted its talents to lacquer and silver filigree; Canton,

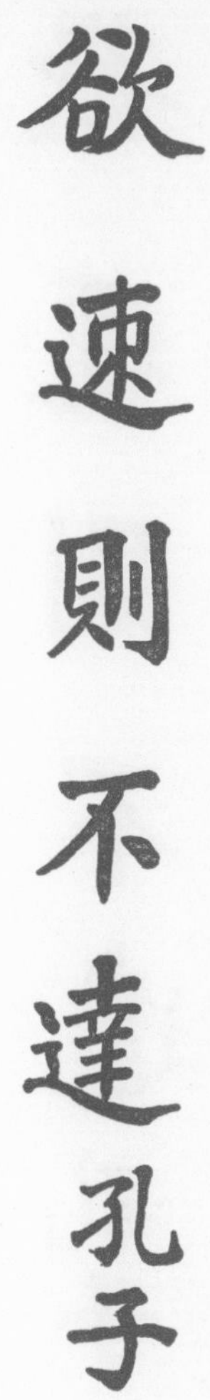

close to southern Asia's elephant herds, carved ivories; and Chengtu, in far-western Szechwan Province, was sought for silk crepe of such beauty and durability that all Occidental attempts to duplicate it in manufacture have proved futile.

The ability to work in crowded quarters with simple tools has made it possible for China to have a small army of peripatetic artisans. Each man has a different call to announce approach, and they move freely through town and countryside with their complete outfits—stands, stoves, tools—packed compactly together in small loads swung from a carrying-pole. Many of them peddle small productions of their craft, but the chief business is mending in this land where no object, however battered or broken, is ever deliberately thrown away.

The commonest criticism of the Chinese artisan is his failure to adapt machinery to his use, but where population is so enormous and the labor market so overcrowded, mass production would seem to offer only a threat to individual security. Better that many men sweat long hours at toil for small recompense than that the few prosper and the majority starve to death, argue the Chinese. Hard work holds no terrors for this industrious race, but insecurity is to be dreaded beyond all other fates. Leave a man his work and he will

不達孔子

endure any and every calamity with fortitude; force idleness upon him and he will end in the depths of misery. So strongly do they feel about the menace of the machine to their ranks that, in a number of cases, where progressive concerns have striven to introduce mechanized methods into inland communities, the workers have met the innovations with destruction.

For countless generations, these humble and tireless craftsmen have given not only to their own land but to the world at large the innumerable results of their strength and skill. Genial and uncomplaining about working conditions and financial returns that have changed little in thousands of years, they have, in the effort to combine beauty and utility in all they make, unwittingly set a standard of diligence and integrity that any civilization might do well to copy. "With patience a block of iron may be worn down to a needle," is one of their commonest sayings. Commissioned to such a task, the Chinese artisan takes a fierce pride in grinding out the finest needle his imagination can picture.

Wu Tailor in *Insects Do Not Bite Busy People* cannot be considered representative of the artisan group, since his line of work was considered on the lower level of industry. This was due to his having to make funeral garments—a circumstance that prevented his ever becoming a candidate for the official examinations, bitter medicine for any Chinese to swallow. But while they might not be scholars, tailors were and are creative artists, as any Western woman resident in China might testify, and except in those localities where they have been too long exposed to foreign influences of speed and carelessness in workmanship, they possess the same virtues as their brothers in other trades.

欲速則不達

孔子

欲速則不達 孔子

霍林路

INSECTS DO NOT BITE BUSY PEOPLE

As he attached the last frog fastener to a long, pongee gown, Wu T'sai-feng (Cut-stitch man) found his mind wandering from its customary worry about debt to the immediate question of whether the steady slap-slap of marching feet to which he had been listening since dawn this rainy summer morning would mean extra work before nightfall. For war, which made people everywhere tighten moneybags until an honest workman became blind searching for profit, had twice in the last moon brought him the additional duties of altering soldiers' uniforms without pay.

Naturally, with the whole nation struggling to resist the "Island Dwarfs," a man wished to help where he could, though Wu sometimes felt that he had done more than a fair share toward patriotism when his first assistant was conscripted for service. The authorities, it was true, had permitted him, the master, no decision in the matter; but the tailor liked to think that this sacrificial gesture had been voluntary, even while his thrifty soul deplored such waste of skill. Certainly, the real value to warfare of one who had spent six years learning to cut and finish garments presented a question which had its humorous as well as dubious side, and the thought of manipulating a bayonet with hands adapted to a needle never failed to twist the other's lips in a wry smile. The absence from this establishment of an experienced helper was not, however, a smiling matter, and at present, Wu, with no one to depend on save his wife, whom Kuan-yin knew had duties enough of her own in the household, and one thirteen-year-old apprentice, could not help but wonder how he could accomplish more work, even if Good Fortune were to send it to his need.

Beh T'sai-feng, ten doors or so up the street and prosperous beyond Wu's dreams, could undoubtedly offer plenty of advice on this state of affairs were he to be consulted. The latter, rotund and oozing pork-fat sweat from every pore, found leisure to call at the most inconvenient moments on the little tailor, whose establishment was so unimportant that even in thought Beh did not dignify the other man by the term competitor. Crowding into the room that was store and workshop combined, Beh would push from the stool on which he had elected to sit, materials that Wu had just carefully arranged there and would then patronizingly air his theories on how to succeed in life.

"I tell you, Honorable T'sai-feng, a man must decide early whether he will spend his own valuable strength every minute or whether others shall spend theirs for him. The second way is mine." Beh would pause for effect before continuing this peroration. "For instance, Wu T'sai-feng stays as close to his shop as any housewife to her mending, is it not so? A poor method, Honorable Tailor, for bringing trade to one's door! Now I, myself, stroll about the city frequently, stopping at teahouses to talk with acquaintances on various matters. Men notice and say, 'Beh's business "down to the ground" must be good! Otherwise he could not wear silk garments and waste time at *wan-wan!*'"

His host, wondering anxiously if three or four feet of cloth had been reckoned in figuring for the sleeveless jacket ready to be cut out, would murmur with simulated admiration, "Truly, Beh T'sai-feng's helpers are well trained that they do good work even when the master is absent!"

This sly thrust, for every tailor in the city knew that Beh's work was of poor quality and that his rise to prosperity had been due to a glib tongue and ingratiating ways, did not even pierce the surface of the guest's complacence. He drew back his lips midway from their journey toward a smiling acknowledgment of this statement, then shrugged as if so many similar compliments had settled on him with the passing of time that he could no longer bother with additional ones. "To conquer difficulties a man needs merely to have a full head. Now Wu T'sai-feng, for example, should not have climbed to that shelf then—for no other purposes are apprentices born! And had those mislaid shears been mine, someone else, not the owner, would have sought them." He yawned, glanced incuriously at a half-finished robe hanging on the wall beside him, then added, "Moreover, My Esteemed Friend, how do you hope to make profit when one half this number of stitches would hold the seam together?"

"After a few wearings, what then?" defended Wu.

"When a garment has been paid for and delivered, why should the tailor squeeze heart in fist? Also, how many people examine workmanship? If they do," Beh gestured broadly with a hand, "the latest gossip from the teahouse will make them forget to complain, is it not so? With foreigners this is easy beyond belief—one pretends only to know little English and to understand none of their Chinese."

Wu, having savored these unpalatable crumbs of advice with growing distaste, drew a breath of relief when the speaker paused abruptly to twitch muscles between his shoulder blades. "Fleas!" complained Beh with a frown, as he rose, slapping at a thigh and moving toward the street, "are worse this summer than I can remember."

"Are they?" asked his host, adding politely, "walk slowly, walk slowly!" and relishing the fact that where fleas, at least, were concerned he was more successful than Beh. His own scrawny body seemed to offer no temptation to pests, and with dry humor, he repeated the old proverb, "Insects do not bite busy people"—a bit of wisdom that must certainly be passed on sometime to his tormentor.

In discouraging contrast to Beh's methods, Wu T'sai-feng told himself this morning, no single one of the immediate tasks before him would net a decent return in silver. Into the pongee gown which awaited pressing, he had put far too many hours for the price agreed upon; the three grass linen robes still to be cut out for the tea merchant were being done at a reduced rate because of previous obligations in that quarter; and the gold thread embroidery on the gauze garment had literally eaten up profit.

Suddenly conscious of quieter surroundings, the tailor forgot unpleasant calculations in noticing through the doorway that the street was now empty of troops. He turned, threw the pongee gown over the pressing board, lit a charcoal fire in the base of the iron, then called to the apprentice, "Lay down that hemming and run to the street for more gold thread!"

Welcoming any task that took him from sewing, this embryo garment maker good-naturedly kicked off worn cotton shoes, rolled trouser legs to knees, and, folding a rag over head and shoulders, stepped outside.

As he disappeared, a foreign woman took his place on the threshold. The proprietor looked up and stared; he had wished so often for this to happen that his eyes seemed now to be tricking him. Foreigners were known to throw silver around as carelessly as if the coins flowered on bean plants, and accordingly, every workman longed for their patronage. With the next breath Wu T'sai-feng recovered his wits, bowed ceremoniously, cleared a seat for the visitor, and a moment later, learned that this foreign teacher had been dissatisfied for some time with the quality of workmanship from an establishment close by, and at the suggestion of a Chinese friend, had come here.

So, in this case at least, carelessness had cost Beh a patron, the little tailor thought to himself as, automatically murmuring, "Most unworthy!" he studied the fashion picture of a blouse, made measurements, calculated labor and cost feverishly, and inquired when the work must be completed.

"By tomorrow at noon," was the calm reply.

"Tomorrow, a thousand pardons for bad ears, but did the Honorable Teacher say, 'tomorrow'?"

"Tomorrow afternoon," the young American woman smiled assent, "I wish to wear this new blouse to Kiukiang. I should have come earlier this morning, had not soldiers crowded the streets."

Listening, Wu T'sai-feng acknowledged to himself the truth of all that had ever been said about the mad haste of barbarians. With the pongee and gauze to be delivered today, and the three linens prepared for fitting, how he would make this foreign *gua-tz* was beyond imagination. However, to hesitate in the face of such opportunity was equally impossible! Bracing thin shoulders, he plunged into the depths of risk. "By tomorrow noon," his lips promised gravely, "the Respected Teacher shall have her garment!"

After the visitor had departed, Wu, still dazed by this surprising introduction to Good Fortune and wondering how he could possibly manage to keep its acquaintance, fingered the material and counted the eight carved ivory buttons to be used as fasteners. Not since his own days as apprentice in Kiukiang had he worked on foreign clothing, and this printed picture must be studied carefully before shears touched the silk. Tomorrow noon—*ai-ya!* Every minute would count toward success.

He sniffed the smell of heat from the iron, and striding toward the rear door, swung it open, called, "Mother of my son, a foreigner brings us a *gua-tz* to be made between breaths, and I need your help!" then turning, began to map out a schedule for the intervening hours.

Later as Wu Wife quietly pushed the long-handled iron over pongee, Wu T'sai-feng cut deftly into the tea merchant's linen and divided his thoughts between answering his companion's questions about the foreigner and dreaming of a future when worry would no longer perch on his rooftree. If the American woman were pleased, she would doubtless tell others in her household and they, in turn, would recommend him to friends. In fancy the little tailor leaped to the head of a large establishment with five or six skilled apprentices at his command.

Dimly conscious of a shadow on this mood, he became aware once more of marching feet. High Heaven grant that none of the soldiers pause here today! A sharp exclamation from his wife further distracted attention. "Look!"

she said, pointing to a spot of water on the pongee's soft sheen.

Wu stepped to her side and squinted upward. As he did so, a drop landed on his nose and two others spattered themselves close to the first on the material. "Since you must leak," the tailor demanded irritably of the roof as he helped move the pressing equipment to safety, "was there no other place than this to choose?" On pongee water stained like grease and the whole panel would have to be sponged, dried, and pressed again.

"Me-me, bring a pan!" called Wu Wife, and a six-year-old daughter hurried in with the article. Behind her, like the unevenly jerking tail to a kite, toddled two younger brothers, one baby pig, and three chickens with clipped wings. While the leak absorbed the attention of their parents and sister, the little boys, attired only in halter-aprons that partially covered their fronts, made straight for that always forbidden goal, the street. The young pig, bent apparently on the same road to freedom, stuck close to their heels and as they neared the exit, unwisely jostled his companions, whose fat-creased legs and ankles were under no restraint to ordinary laws of balance. A sudden thud, attended by cries and squeals, brought both father and mother hurrying across the room to comfort their offspring and to rescue the struggling animal from the tangle of arms and legs threatening its extinction.

Meanwhile the fowls, usually barred from this room, had been enjoying their unexpected visit by picking at ends of thread and other colorful items on the dirt floor. The cock among these, whose long neck and scraggly feathers gave it a peculiar resemblance to Wu T'sai-feng, himself, stretched curiously to see what might be found on a near-by stool, then with a flapping of wings, landed on top. There it skidded about on a soft pile of silk crepe and noted with special interest several small, hard objects rolling between its toes. Desire grew in the bird's eyes and in another moment one of the shining spheres was in its bill. Swallowing the trophy required more effort than had been expected and as the chicken stood there gulping, Wu, who had been drying his younger son's angry tears, now gave the small boy a final pat on bare buttocks and turned in the direction of the stool. Horrified at sight of the fowl on the foreigner's material, he shooed the squawking trespasser to the floor and through the rear doorway.

Careful examination of the silk revealed claw impressions and several dirty scratches. Clutching the ivory buttons in his left fist and muttering breathlessly to himself, the tailor worked to erase the damage. When this was done satisfactorily, he folded the goods in an extra wrapping, laid it on a shelf, then counted the buttons before tying them together in a rag. At the result his eyelids blinked. Slowly, fingering each one, Wu reckoned again, "*Ih*, *er*, *san*, *si*, *wu*, *luh, chi—chi!*" Seven, but where was the eighth? Of a certainty, there had been eight buttons! What then? The next few moments were spent in a wild search for the missing object through the mass of materials, partially made garments, and countless odds and ends common to a tailoring workroom.

His wife, waiting for the pongee panel to dry, called out, "What do you seek?"

"The foreigner's button—like these," Wu told her with a wild expression in his eye. "Eight there were and seven remain, with no other of their kind nearer than Kwangtung, a thousand miles away. *Ai-ya*, that I should have lived to see this day! Fortune brings me a rich foreigner's trade and I ruin her first garment before I touch it!"

"Those buttons—where did you find them?" she interrupted.

"Where did I find them?" demanded Wu irascibly. "Woman, did I not say they were the foreigner's?"

"Yes, yes, but where in this room?"

"On the stool with the silk!" he shouted, then stood suddenly speechless in the grip of memory. That fowl's throat had been working when he chased it off the stool! "*Ai!*" he gasped, lifting a hand to his brow, "*ai*, the chicken!"

Bewildered, his wife parroted vaguely, "Chicken—what chicken?"

"Our cock ate the button."

"You are certain?"

"Down to the ground! Bring me that bird from hell that I may wring its neck and get my button."

"Patience!" Wu Mistress protested. "Do we wish no more eggs from the hens? I have a plan: until the *gua-tz* is finished, you need no buttons. Therefore, I cage the fowl, feeding it a little medicine to hasten matters."

Wu frowned. "What affair is this?"

"Lay down your heart! In due time the button shall be returned—is that not Nature's way?" With this philosophical comment his wife proceeded to her task.

Wu moved again to the cutting board and nervously resumed work. A turtle's progress, indeed, on all there was to do. "Did you think this a feast day that you spend an hour buying thread?" he demanded as the apprentice now crossed the threshold. "Climb to the roof and move the tiles over that leak!"

The boy looked dubious. "While rain falls?"

"When the clouds cease emptying buckets, the roof will no longer leak—is it not so?" his master inquired sarcastically, then relenting added, "later, you shall have a bowl of hot tea!"

With a sigh of resignation, the apprentice slipped again into the downpour; Wu Mistress returned to her pressing, and Wu cut into the second of the tea merchant's gowns.

For a brief moment peace settled over the workroom, then swiftly disappeared as the owner of the gauze garment entered.

"My third daughter who went 'through the gate' a month ago," the new arrival announced after exchange of greetings, "returns today for a visit, accompanied by others from her husband's home. Naturally, I wish my new robe."

"Naturally," repeated Wu. "Would that it were completed!"

The customer's eyebrows lifted. "Your promise was for today, is it not so?"

"Truly, but at evening, not noontide!"

The other pondered this gravely, then suggested, "A small favor I ask: that you finish my robe before those whose owners have not such great need."

Wu's thoughts ran with mad speed around the groove of duties. This man was not a very good customer, but to refuse his request might send him away forever. "Can do," the tailor agreed after a moment or two, then addressed his wife, "When the pongee is pressed, stitch the gold thread on that collar."

"And in an hour I return, *hao puh hao?*" inquired the satisfied patron.

"Three!" corrected Wu.

"Three?"

"Three—I have said it!"

Wet and smudged with dirt, the apprentice now returned from the roof. His master, glancing after the departing customer gave the boy one look and cautioned fearfully, "Go wash yourself clean!"

"And the bowl of tea?"

Wu Wife interrupted, "Blow the ashes to life under the water kettle and I will come!" Lifting the pongee garment from the pressing board, she folded and wrapped it carefully for delivery, then turned toward the kitchen.

Shortly afterwards the apprentice, cleaner and warmed by the hot drink, came in for further orders. Wu threw him a short smile. "Your fortune is bad today, for now you must carry that garment to the home of Chi Hsien-Seng on the Street of Eleven Gates."

Before the words had died on his lips, Chi Hsien-Seng, himself, accompanied by a young man, appeared in the doorway. As they exchanged greetings, the tailor's spirits rose—this would, at least, release the boy for other tasks. But with Chi's next remark, hope of saving time faded.

"I call for my garment and at the same time bring you a new customer, T'sai-feng," he announced. "This moon my nephew visits me and while here wishes to take advantage of your workmanship. When you have measured him, then we go on the street to buy materials."

Wu expressed deep appreciation, torn between delight over new trade and worry about this day's succession of delays. He must hurry this affair without seeming to do so, for Chi was not given to unseemly haste in anything and resented it in others. A half hour later the three were still involved in discussing the merits of variously styled garments for the visitor, Chi becoming momentarily more genial and the proprietor more glum. The latter's mind was in a turmoil over the passing of time, and when water suddenly splashed on them where they stood, Wu vented his feelings by bawling to the apprentice, "Another leak! Climb up and fix it!"

To add to irritation, the owner of the gauze robe now presented himself again. "A little early, I am," he admitted pleasantly, "but I thought the work might be ready before you said."

Fuming inwardly Wu threw the latter a heated glance, but managed to say quietly, "One and one half hours are not three!"

The other man sat down silently to wait and as he did so, Wu Wife came from the rear carrying a limp fowl in her arms. "I fear the cock dies!" she announced without further ado.

"Then of a certainty I get my button!" her husband replied mercilessly.

"Button?" asked Chi staring in curiosity from tailor to chicken.

The waiting customer now rose and joined the others and for a time everything else was forgotten in the unusual problem which Wu Wife falteringly brought to their attention. The proprietor, alone, showed no interest. He stood like a figure of doom through all their conversation, chained by courtesy to his patron's side until Chi, himself, should terminate the business.

"Mothers!" Wu cursed furiously in silence while his mind beat out the duties demanding attention and his fingers itched to get at the work. Before this day was done, he would undoubtedly be crazed. What then would his children do? Beg on the streets, he supposed, or die of starvation! He, himself, in that case would go to the grave with no one to remember his name at ancestral tablets—and for what reason? A sick chicken! What did this woman of his mean wasting important time on such nonsense? Let the fowl die and give back the button! No, she must try to save it that they might have future eggs from the hens. In the future—*ai*, this house would probably know no future! For himself he wished there were no present and that he had never seen the foreign woman or her blouse! This was the end—this!

Chi Hsien-Seng's voice broke in on these lugubrious thoughts, "Who can say whether your medicine or the button kills the bird, Good Wife?" he offered in consolation.

"What is most important is that the fowl still lives," the nephew stated judiciously. "Perhaps a few drops of warm tea down its throat might help."

His uncle smiled approval, but the owner of the gauze gown, since the suggestion had not been his, looked dubious.

"Yes, yes, yes—a little warm tea, a little warm tea!" Wu broke in, grasping frantically at any opportunity to change the present inactivity, but his wife stood where she was pondering the young man's advice.

To the two uniformed men who now leaned in the doorway, the room presented a surprising picture. True, there were some evidences of the tailoring establishment which they had been led to expect, but neither workmen nor apprentices were to be seen. Instead, while rain dripped in dismal monotony from a leaking roof, four men and a woman stood silently in the foreground lost in concentration over what seemed to be a dead chicken. For a long breath the two soldiers stared at each other. Finally one muttered, "If this be the best tailoring shop in town, I am still an unhatched egg!" then stepped inside and demanded abruptly, "Does a tailor, called Wu, dwell here?"

Like a man already certain of ruin, Wu T'sai-feng now heard final sentence pronounced. The evil which he had feared from dawn of this fateful day had at last found him. "Sirs," he replied with sincerity, as his wife promptly disappeared and the three customers sought less conspicuous positions in the shadows, "I am that miserable one."

"Our men follow with uniforms to be altered. How soon can you do the work?"

"How many garments?" the proprietor asked in dull resignation. Gone forever was his hope of foreign trade—truly the gods had played with him this day!

"Ten or more—collars and sleeves!"

"I have only two hands and such work eats time."

"Where are your helpers?"

"My assistant fights for our country; otherwise there is but one apprentice and most of his stitches would trip a water buffalo."

"This tailor speaks truly?" an officer now turned to inquire of Chi.

"Truly, indeed!"

"Is there another of his trade near by?"

"Beh who has seven helpers lives but a few doors away," Wu informed them in a voice robbed of animation.

The soldiers frowned and moved restlessly aside to weigh these obstacles in private discussion. Their captain had sent them here because of this man's reputation for good work. If he could not alter the coats swiftly, however, what then? Perhaps, they should leave him a few of the garments and take the rest to Beh. As they reached this decision, a sudden, startling downpour descended on their heads from the roof above and the two military representatives forgot dignity and form in jumping hastily aside. "That is enough!" one exclaimed in disgust. "Only a fool would have recommended this place to our captain.

We risk no uniforms here! First dead chickens, then floods —a tailoring shop, indeed!" In high dudgeon they passed into the street.

Chi and his nephew soon followed and shortly afterwards the customer with his gauze garment. Under the stimulation of hot tea the fowl revived; the apprentice returned to work; and the tea merchant sent a note saying that he would delay his fitting until the weather improved. With a growing sense of reprieve, Wu at last sat down to study the picture of the foreign blouse. The eighth button was still missing, but his wife continued to counsel patience in that matter and by the time evening rice was served the American's garment lay in carefully measured sections ready for sewing.

Later, belching loud appreciation of food, the apprentice fitted the sliding panels to the shop front and joined his master in the task before them. At the Hour of the Pig, Wu Wife came into the quiet room and extended one palm on which lay a carved ivory button seemingly little the worse for having traveled so unusual a journey. "Did I not say it was Nature's way?" she asked her husband, then without waiting for reply, added, "The children sleep; now let me help a little."

Grunting to himself, Wu took the button and handed her a sleeve in exchange. Trying indeed was this woman of his sometimes, but of great value nevertheless! Not only had she given him two sons, but her thrift and industry were beyond description—and he would choose no other in her place.

Through most of the night the three sewed diligently, until weariness at last threatened the quality of work. In the morning there would be sufficient time to finish the garment satisfactorily. When the pieces were folded neatly, Wu rose, stretched, and peered beneath heavy eyelids at the ceiling. "You stopped those leaks well," he told the apprentice; "that one when the soldiers were here threatened to drown us."

The boy's yawns were smothered in a chuckle. "Of a certainty!" Rubbing his eyes, he went on. "I had just moved the tile over the little leak when my foot slipped. For a moment I thought I was killed. Learning to breathe again, I saw through the narrow crack that the military stood just beneath. They did not like our shop," he paused to dart a questioning glance at his master before continuing. "Quickly, I lifted all of the tiles I could reach." A mischievous grin washed sleep from his face. "*Ai*—but they jumped!"

Wu T'sai-feng stared at the boy in admiration. "And I thought you were of no use! So good a plan it was—I forget a thousand mistakes. Now go to sleep!"

Shortly after noon the following day, Wu proceeded lightheartedly down the street toward home. In his moneybag lay the foreigner's silver and in memory, her words of appreciation and promise of more work. Yesterday, he told himself, had undoubtedly aged him five years, but its difficulties were now in the past and the future looked brighter than ever before. Passing Beh's, he caught a glimpse of that worthy seated gloomily within his shop. Contrary to custom, the little tailor paused and, stepping inside, exchanged greetings. Noting the feverish industry of all present, Wu commented with an innocent air, "Small wonder that you prosper, Honorable T'sai-feng. Always your shop is crowded with work!"

"Work!" snorted Beh. "Truly—in plenty and at no profit! Look a look!"

The guest obeyed. Uniforms were not only occupying each man's attention, but others were piled along the shelves. "Tchk! Tchk!" Wu's tongue clicked, then comforted soothingly, "Beh Tailor acquires much merit in thus helping the army."

For a moment Beh's jowls reddened as if with apoplexy. "Merit—a fine thing while my regular customers wait for their garments!" He poured out his bitterness. "Yesterday while I attended a feast, the military came and, finding no one in authority, settled like a swarm of locusts on my shop. This morning they returned with more coats. When I spoke of previous orders, those rotten eggs dared to tell me, 'If the proprietor can go to feasts and his men spend the hours at dominoes—surely there is time to serve the government!'" He spat a furious period to this speech, then repeated, "Like locusts, and there is no way to be free of them!"

Wu expressed understanding and bowed his departure. As he stepped on the curb, he murmured to himself, "Insects do not bite busy people!"

"What did you say?" Beh called after him.

"See you again—see you again," the other returned over his shoulder and, smiling dryly, hurried toward home.

巧言令色鮮矣仁孔子

THE COOLIE

Fine garments and flowery speech are no proofs of virtue.

From several authentic sources we are told that the word, "coolie," is a pidgin English term brought into use by foreigners within the past two centuries. In certain inland sections of China, however, the expression most commonly used to describe these laborers who are the burden bearers for a nation is *chi ku tih ren*, which being translated means "eating-bitterness-people," and one wonders if the term *ku*, or "bitterness," might not have been appropriately seized upon for the first syllable of a name for that class of individuals which, from the cradle to the grave, lives at the whims of other, more fortunate men. What however might seem to discount this theory is the fact that for a great many years along the foreignized coast line stretching from Tsingtao to Singapore, "coolie" was a synonym for contempt. With that blindness to reality which in the old days seemed the birthright of the average American or European in the East, this lowly laborer was cataloged as stupid, dishonest, and corrupt, and like the citizens of ancient Nazareth, no good could possibly be expected of him. In the more enlightened present, it seems beyond belief that such ideas could ever have been formulated, for the coolie, indispensable cog in the Far Eastern scheme of living, is not only amazingly honest and decent, but he also meets life with an ingenuity that is the envy of the world.

He it is who carries most of the country's merchandise from one section to another; who brings food, and in rural districts where modern conveniences do not yet prevail, water to every door. He performs all menial tasks about house or business, runs errands, digs the gardens, becomes the horse for small vehicles, disposes of undesirable refuse, and where the foreigner in particular is concerned, often does his master's thinking for him in the latter's task of adaptation to the Orient.

Usually, the coolie renders these services with remarkable efficiency. He is convinced that the foreigner is a *rara avis* who can never be counted upon to follow a natural or reasonable course of action, and in his contacts with the other he must learn to be startled by nothing; to endure crudities to which his own countrymen would never subject him; to meet demands which often seem as unfathomable as the grave, and at the same time to keep his own self-respect, or "face."

Of the mass, however, the individuals who lift themselves into the personal servant class whether among

巧言令色鮮矣仁
孔子

巧言令色鮮矣仁

孔子

foreigners or Chinese, are few indeed, and their more fortunate circumstances are in no way representative of those of the many millions of load-bearers, chair-carriers, wheelbarrow-pushers, and ricksha-runners who fill up the ranks. These are the men who almost never have hunger fully appeased; whose homes are a ludicrous exaggeration of the word "shelter"; whose clothing, too often a thin cotton jacket and trousers for all weather, is patched until the patches themselves hang in overlapping shreds, and whose bodies, still young in years, grow gnarled and twisted from exposure and the strain of superhuman toil.

Their vocabulary is limited to three or four hundred words, and conversation of necessity deals chiefly with wages and food. Having lived always on the dregs, they seldom ask favors of Fortune. To owe less debt this year than last; to help their children escape some of the worst hardships and afflictions; to hope personally for a decent burial, and for the present moment, to find means for a bit of tobacco or a taste of meat in the daily rice and vegetable—these sum up desire for the average among them.

The Occidental giving serious consideration to such living conditions would unreservedly decide in favor of nonexistence, but the Chinese coolie has through centuries of fighting for the right to live acquired a philosophy that includes the ability to laugh easily, to admire beauty and goodness, and to return abundantly any crumbs of kindness or understanding that fall his way. Facing disaster beyond his usual wretchedness, he beats his breast for a night only. With the coming of dawn, courage is renewed from some inexhaustible source deep within him, and, pulling together his tattered remnants of squalor, he goes forth gallantly to meet the burden of another day.

That Lao-Cheo in *The Head of His House* is a fairly accurate portrayal of a Chinese servant in an average foreign home, I believe a good many Westerners would agree. Born to squalor and illiteracy, he had managed through almost fifty years of hardship and unceasing toil to preserve integrity, unquenchable humor, and single-minded devotion to the interests of those he served. The fact that coolies, such as this man, come from the lower strata of existence provides one of the most remarkable commentaries on Chinese civilization as a whole.

巧言令色鮮矣仁

孔子

巧言令色鮮矣仁　孔子

霍林路

THE HEAD OF HIS HOUSE

Lao-Cheo, the coolie, puttering in the strawberry bed in the Mission Compound, caught at his back and rubbed briskly. He would have something to say to that doctor at Han-Si-Men about the pain that came with stooping—had not the man been paid in advance to ward off troubles such as this? At Hwa-Pai-Lo there was another healer, it was rumored, who, although he prescribed strong, unpleasant doses, made short shrift of the devils of disease. The idea of consulting this other, however, must not reach the ears of the American *Si-Mu*, Lao-Cheo decided. Once she learned about this cramp in his back, she would insist that he go, instead, to the foreign doctor at the University Dispensary, and while foreigners did well enough with surface cuts and bruises, even stupid folk knew better than to trust the outsiders with more serious troubles.

The garden, soaked from weeks of rain, steamed in the hot sun. Lifting his head, the coolie breathed deeply the odor of fruit blossoms. His glance traveled along a bar of sunshine through the study window of the house a few feet away, just as the *Hsien-Seng* withdrew an arm from the *Si-Mu's* shoulders. The spectator's eyelids blinked. He reached for his hoe. Never would he become accustomed to some of the foreign ways!

Five years he, himself, had lived with a wife, and little of his time had been wasted on displays of affection. *Ai*, what a temper had been hers! He had considered himself favored of heaven when, through eating fish that was none too fresh, she had "ascended the Dragon" to join her ancestors in the spirit world. At this unexpected release, his relief was so great that he had never remarried—and this in spite of the bargains with which certain old women in the trade approached him. He knew when he was well off. The *Hsien-Seng* and *Si-Mu* were kindly, and except for such foolishness as that just witnessed, they did not lack wisdom. Had they not learned to speak Chinese so that the Chinese, themselves, understood it? Moreover, the *Si-Mu's* temper was not too easily fired, although she sometimes grew excited when, in the business of polishing floors, he confused the scrub mop with the one that was oiled. But this was a trifle; if necessary he could overlook much greater annoyances for the sake of living under the same roof with their little girl.

In his opinion girl-children had never been of any importance and until now he had paid small attention to them. This three-year-old, though, with the dark curls and bright eyes was different from most. When he called, "Doloty!" she would leave even the amah to run to him. Indeed, he told himself for the hundredth time, there was no single fault to be found in this little maid, save that of not being a boy.

He broke the earth, his mind turning from these pleasant channels to the more serious business of trying to remember the pen strokes in the characters, Nan-Ching. Since the *Hsien-Seng* had opened the night school for servants, Lao-Cheo had attended regularly. Forty-seven years of his life had passed and he was doing books for the first time. At the last session the Classics teacher had complimented him on his ability to learn. Of course, he was not swift, but scholars were always deliberate! Only fools and foreigners rushed madly through life. Added to this commendation had been his own discovery that the pursuit of knowledge increased one's personal prestige, as well as wisdom; already he had derived real pleasure from showing the cook that that worthy was no longer the only servant in this household who could write.

Straightening to wipe away perspiration with the tail of his blue cotton jacket, he felt his heart thud. For the moment, he could have sworn his eyes had seen that rotten egg, Hsiao-Cheo, in a distant corner of the compound. He watched intently, but no further movement rewarded him, and after a moment the hoeing was resumed. Blossoming fruit trees often cast grotesque shadows, and Hsiao-Cheo had been on his heart so much lately, that he was imagining him everywhere.

The youth was the son of his dead brother. With the latter's death, Lao-Cheo had become the legal head of the family and, accepting responsibility, he had asked the *Hsien-Seng*, when a vacancy occurred, to hire this nephew as a school servant. Four months after Hsiao-Cheo secured the position, twenty dollars disappeared from the school's office. The *Hsien-Seng* and the new employee, alone, possessed keys to that particular room, but Hsiao-Cheo, cross-examined with the other servants, had denied any knowledge of the theft. He admitted only that he had neglected to lock the office the preceding evening until dusk, and during that period the thief must have entered.

Lao-Cheo had listened and made no comment while the younger man gave testimony. Recently this nephew had been acquiring bad habits, but one does not lightly suspect a member of his own family of having itching palms. Avoiding the youth, the uncle had gone, instead, straight from the questioning to the chief source of lagging feet and bloodshot eyes in the community—Dsu, cook in the foreign house at the corner of the street. With a little well-chosen flattery there had finally been drawn from this seasoned gambler the admission that Hsiao-Cheo had been losing heavily at the dominoes, but had somehow contrived to settle for his mistakes.

With his worst fears confirmed, Lao-Cheo had returned to the compound only to have the *Hsien-Seng* call him and Hsiao-Cheo again to the study. Throughout life the memory of that conversation would remain painfully clear.

Hsiao-Cheo's continued denial of any fault but negligence had been followed by the *Hsien-Seng's* question directed to the youth, "And can you explain, perhaps, how a man who earns only twenty-four dollars in four months of working, can settle a nineteen-dollar debt in one payment?"

To this accusation Hsiao-Cheo had attempted no reply. The uncle, realizing that the foreigner knew all, heard his own voice lie in a desperate effort to save the family name, "I lent the silver to him."

Silence ensued. The *Hsien-Seng* had seemed suddenly interested in a scroll on the opposite wall, while the culprit, bound to immobility by this net of his own weaving, stared into space. With difficulty Lao-Cheo had pulled further dry words from his throat, "My nephew admits he forgot to lock the office, therefore responsibility for the missing silver is on his body—and on mine. If the *Hsien-Seng's* kindness permits so great a favor, we would have half our wages held each month until the account is paid. In the future he will be more careful—that I promise!"

The foreigner had listened, his gaze still concentrated on the scroll's delicately pictured landscape. For a fleeting moment he studied the youth's motionless figure thoughtfully, then in an effort to save face for all concerned, accepted the older coolie's terms.

Later, alone with his nephew, Lao-Cheo had released his bitterness. "I know, and the *Hsien-Seng* knows, the truth.

Because I did not want our name connected with dirty fingers, I told him I gave you the money. One thing you will remember—not again do you visit Dsu's kitchen! Now go to your work."

Disappointment, as well as anger, had eaten at the older man's heart; his hope had been that this nephew might be as a son to him. And then, two weeks later, Hsiao-Cheo had disappeared, leaving his uncle to bear the shame of the broken contract. With a rare depth of understanding the *Hsien-Seng* had asked no questions and had hired another coolie, but Lao-Cheo suffered none the less from the blow.

A sudden call from the nurse now released him from these moody memories. "Lao-Cheo, have you seen Small Sister?"

Without turning he grunted a denial. Amah was a widow who wished to remarry, and the wisest course for any man was to ignore her completely.

"Have you seen Bé-Bé?" the woman repeated shrilly.

"No!" he shouted. "I——" But Amah was already running as fast as her hobbled feet would carry her toward the house. Amazed, he looked after her. Ordinarily the amah moved slowly, and when provoked, it was her habit to state in no uncertain terms her opinion of his brusqueness.

"Lao-Cheo," the *Hsien-Seng* called next, "search the shrubbery for Dorothy while I look over the school grounds! Amah left the baby for a minute in the garden and now she is not to be found."

"Perhaps the house!" the coolie started to suggest.

"No, we have been all over the house, and Lao-Wu says she has not gone through the gate. See if she is hiding among the bushes while I search the school."

The shrubbery revealed no trace of the missing three-year-old. With a sinking heart Lao-Cheo thought of the cistern outside the kitchen. When he reached the spot—Kuan-yin be thanked—the heavy stone slab still covered its surface! The woodshed was empty; the doors to the servant quarters fastened securely; the rear gate locked. Over and over he cried the child's name, "Doloty! Doloty!" In another moment she would come dancing out to him, the dark eyes alive with mischief, the tiny fingers ready to wind about his gnarled ones. He no longer hunted with design; his feet hurried aimlessly from one place to the next.

"Lao-Cheo, have you found her?"

Panic's chilling fingers gripped the coolie's mind. "Not yet! Not yet!" he managed to reply. "Truly, she must have gone through the gate—Lao-Wu often dozes. I go on the street to see!"

"This time Lao-Wu did not sleep," contradicted the *Hsien-Seng* flatly. "For the past hour he has been talking with a food vendor in the gateway; unlikely is it that the child passed without their knowing. The other servants are already inquiring at neighboring compounds and I myself, go now to further the search outside. Wu can remain at the gate while you stay here—it is still my hope that she may be somewhere within these walls."

In a daze Lao-Cheo watched the Master leave the compound; he saw the *Si-Mu,* her shoulders shaking, re-enter the house; he heard the amah call "Bé-Bé! Bé-Bé!" wildly from room to room. For the moment he seemed paralyzed by the question of where to turn next.

Then without conscious effort he moved toward the south wall of the garden. In that corner shadowed by persimmon trees his tortured imagination had, only an hour ago, made him see Hsiao-Cheo. Suppose the figure had been real—what then? Baldly the bitter truth presented itself. There before his eyes, strands of ivy torn from a many-fingered hold upon the wall, hung low. Strands freshly torn! He studied the rough plastered surface and saw that it would not be too difficult to climb. But what had such a feat to do with him, Lao-Cheo, or with the foreign child? Had not the *Hsien-Seng* told him to continue hunting here in the compound, and was he suddenly after years of obeying orders now to turn and follow his own will? His thoughts did not even shape an answer. Hsiao-Cheo, the son of his dead brother, and Doloty, who had given a new meaning to life, were both involved in this affair. He straightened. Of what importance were foreigners or their rules in comparison with ancestral duties? In another moment he had scaled the wall and landed on the opposite side.

Before a group of mud huts children sprawled with a litter of pigs. A woman, old and apparently deaf, sat in a doorway sifting grain. She pointed him to others in a sun-drenched field.

As Lao-Cheo approached this group, a man paused in plowing to greet: "*Chi ko fan mo?*"

"I have eaten. And you?"

The worker nodded, adding, "Does the foreign teacher no longer have a gate on the street that the helpers in his household must climb a wall?"

"This back wall is a shorter way to my home near the Water Gate."

"And the youth with the girl-child, this morning—what of him?"

The coolie's heart raced at this, but he answered calmly, "My roof covers him, also."

"Strange to see a young man wasting time with a daughter! Has he no sons?"

"None—great is his misfortune!"

The farmer's tongue clicked sympathetically, and Lao-Cheo, wishing him peace and good crops, hurried along the narrow path.

So Hsiao-Cheo had Doloty. The problem now was to find them. To say that their home was near the Water Gate had been simply an invention of the moment. Whom did his nephew know in this section—who that would dare to shelter a stolen foreign child? Hsiao-Cheo's Nanking acquaintance was limited to a few servants. The uncle checked them off mentally. Giao! He believed that Giao lived at this end of the city. And Giao, having been dismissed by the *Si-Mu* for insolence, would be glad to strike back if opportunity offered.

He soon reached the end of the fields. Entering a busy thoroughfare, he inquired at the first hot-water shop, "Do you recognize among your customers one named Giao?"

"The brass dealer, five houses below."

"No other?"

The shopkeeper scratched his head. "There is a woman who weaves tapestries. She comes here to buy water. I do not know her husband, but she dwells, I believe, in the first cross street to the left. Where, her neighbors can tell you."

Lao-Cheo sought the house and rapped sharply on the panels. From behind a closed door someone demanded his name and business. Instantly he recognized Giao's nasal tones, but this knowledge was no proof that his nephew was within.

"I wish to speak with Cheo Si-Fu," he ventured.

"He does not dwell here."

"That much I know! Tell him I, his uncle, have come."

There was an angry reply. "We know nothing of Cheo, or of his affairs."

Lao-Cheo hesitated. He could not demand entrance merely on the strength of personal suspicion. And then settling all doubts, a child's whimpering reached him—a child who mingled Chinese and foreign syllables in speech. He raised a hand and hammering on the door, demanded, "Let me in at once, or I go straight to the *Ya-men!*"

There was whispering. A crack opened between panels and the coolie pushed through. Before a loom sat the weaver of tapestries holding the child. Lao-Cheo crossed the room and stretched out his arms. Sobbing with fright, Dorothy crept into them. Giao and his wife vanished. Hsiao-Cheo tried to lose himself in the shadows on a wall.

After placing the child gently on a bed, his uncle faced him. "What were your mother's ancestors like, thief? That you do not resemble your father is certain. The Cheo family is poor, but its men live honestly. Stand where you are!" he ordered brusquely as the other started to move, "I have not finished.

"When you took the foreigner's money, I told myself it was the natural folly of youth—Dsu had led others into evil ways. I thought that first experience would teach you wisdom. My heart warmed to you and I forgave easily. Then you ran away!" He spat on the floor. "I was left to face the foreign teacher. The debt I could bear; your shame I could not. Today you stole a second time—not money, but his child. Did you think he would forgive that, as well? Heaven was kind; I saw you and followed."

Sullenly Hsiao-Cheo interrupted, his words tumbling over each other. "I left because I had no face. Dsu and the others taunted; the *Hsien-Seng* distrusted me; you watched everything I did. I wandered about the city, living on a few coppers. This morning something led me back. Quietly I climbed the wall. No one saw me. You were hoeing. I heard the *Hsien-Seng* laugh. A strange servant worked about the school. It was too much to bear. If I could frighten them a little, perhaps they would no longer call me a stupid fool. Amah had been playing beneath a ginkgo tree with the child. Suddenly she left her for a moment to go into the house. It was then the plan came to me. I coaxed the girl-child to me by promising to buy sesame-seed candy on the street and lifted her over the wall. At that minute the amah began calling. I was frightened. I wanted to put the child back, but dared not. I did not know what to do with her, until I remembered Giao."

"And now?"

Hsiao-Cheo raised eyes full of fear. "The foreigner?"

"The foreigner will not learn the truth of this. Is it not enough that he knows a Cheo stole silver? You are a fool, and weak! You were not meant to live in a city where mischief is ready to your hand. Tomorrow, the morning launch will carry you to Wuhu. From there you will walk to our native village and remain to work on a cousin's farm. Those who till the soil have little time for idleness and you may yet learn to care for our name."

The young man's face became distorted by emotion. "I will not go! I am not a child. Who will make me?"

"Have your actions been those of a man?" his uncle's voice whipped out. "I, Cheo Hun Deh, will make you! Am I not the head of our house, fool? You will obey my word, or I will kill you!"

"The law would protect me," Hsiao-Cheo stammered, but his tone held no assurance.

The older man smiled coldly. "When did the Government ever interfere with family law?" he asked.

From the bed the child cried out sleepily, and Lao-Cheo reached for her, raising the little body to his shoulder. "Tonight," he continued, "I will go to the bathhouse on the Great Horse Road at a quarter-point past the ninth hour, by the foreign clock. There I will give you ticket money and further directions." At the door he turned once more to say, "Do not fail to meet me! Otherwise, what I have promised that I will do!"

On the way home he changed rickshas three times so that no runner should furnish contradictory statements regarding where he had found the child. Close to the compound he dismissed the last of these and walked the few remaining yards. Through the gate and up the broad path to the veranda he continued steadily. Figures ran toward him shouting questions. The *Hsien-Seng* appeared, stared as though he dared not believe his own eyes, then strode forward. Lifting the sleeping child from the coolie's arms, he ran into the house, calling exultantly, "Margaret! Margaret! Lao-Cheo has found the baby."

Lao-Cheo followed the father slowly to the door of the living room. Pressing about him, the other servants plied him with questions, but he made no replies. His body was shaking as if with chill; he felt inexpressibly old and tired.

Dispersing the others to their tasks, the *Hsien-Seng* ushered Lao-Cheo into the room, then closed the door.

"Where did you find her? We had inquired everywhere, even to notifying the Consul. No one had seen her."

In a fan-backed chair the *Si-Mu*, smoothing the dark head to her breast, wept her relief. Lao-Cheo eyed mother and child thoughtfully, then turned to the man. "She was near the Han Gate," he replied.

"The Han Gate? But we went there first!"

"I found her in an alley." That statement, at least, was true. "When I call her name, she comes," he added simply.

"And to think that I told you, of all the household, to stay here! Why did you leave?" asked the Master curiously. "You never disobeyed orders before."

"The child was not in the compound—and I had to see for myself." This much would he tell them and no more.

The *Hsien-Seng* looked straight into his coolie's eyes. "You understand, do you not, that we can never repay you?" Then, aware of the embarrassing possibilities of his next statement, he murmured, "Not again is that little affair of the school debt to be remembered."

Lao-Cheo listened gravely. "Most unworthy am I of the *Hsien-Seng's* kindness," he protested. "As for the debt, that is a responsibility of my house and if the foreign Master permits, I shall settle it."

The other man nodded understanding, then ventured: "Your nephew—where is he at present?"

"In our native village, he will become a farmer."

Struggling for control, the *Si-Mu* now interrupted, "Lao-Cheo, we——" her voice broke, "we have no words to thank you."

"What I did was little, Mistress!" He paused, then went on, "A great favor I ask: will the *Si-Mu* grant me this evening for my own use that I may study characters and later go on the street to buy a bath?"

"Of course!" the American woman smiled up at him. "Also, when you have difficulty with lessons, you must tell me and I will ask Li Scholar to help you."

Lao-Cheo expressed appreciation and bowing himself from the room went straight to his own quarters. There he fastened the door firmly against inquisitive companions. No more questions should be answered now! He reached for a pipe and the Primer. So he, the coolie, could have the *Si-Mu's* personal teacher to help him, if necessary! With relish he foresaw the cook's surprised discomfiture at this news. He puffed at the thimbleful of tobacco. After this lesson had been prepared, he would eat evening rice and then meet Hsiao-Cheo at the bathhouse. With Nanking's evil ways forgotten in the demands of farmwork, his nephew might even yet become a man.

And Doloty—Doloty—was safe! His eyes softened at the memory of the small form pressed against his shoulder. Not again would he tempt the Gods by wishing her a boy! He put aside the pipe and began to study the strokes necessary for writing the characters, Nan-Ching.

THE SCHOLAR

The study of books excels all other pursuits.

萬般皆下品惟有讀書高
古詩

There is a bravery characteristic of the sage. . . . boldly to carry into practice his views of the doctrines of the ancient kings; in a high situation not to defer to a bad sovereign, and in a low situation not to follow the current of a bad people; to consider that there is no poverty where there is virtue, and no wealth or honor where virtue is not; when appreciated by the world, to desire to share in all men's joys and sorrows; when unknown by the world, to stand up grandly alone between heaven and earth and have no fears—this is the bravery of the highest order.

—*Hsun K'uang, Translated by James Legge*

Chinese civilization, through most of its history, has been built on the social structure of four main classes: Scholars, Farmers, Artisans, and Merchants. The Scholar held first place because his labors contributed to the mind and spirit of the nation; the Farmer, second, for sustaining the body; the Artisan, third, for fashioning beauty and utility from materials supplied by others; and the Merchant, fourth, since he merely exchanged in barter the products of other men's toil. Below these classifications were listed Soldiers, Actors, Barbers, and a number of other groups whose activities,

萬般皆下品惟有讀書高古詩

for one reason or another, excluded them from the more dignified strata of existence and established their ineligibility as entrants to the official examinations, China's remarkable civil service system.

When scholars first achieved pre-eminence among their compatriots is not definitely known, but the man usually accepted as China's earliest intellectual leader is Tsang Chi, who in the reign of the mythical Yellow Emperor (2697 B.C.) is said to have originated Chinese writing by drawing in ideographs, miniature duplicates of the objects to be designated. Numerous references to teachers and thinkers occur in the later, but also unauthenticated, period of the good kings, Yao and Shun (2350-2250 B.C.), and the ancient *Book of Rites*, one of the thirteen Chinese Classics, states that periodically communities were combed for youths of intelligence, general information, and irreproachable character. Such young men were presented to the king's official examiner, who sent the most promising among them to a school for specialized study, and from this institution to various posts in government service.

Not until the reign of Tai Chung, of the T'ang Dynasty (A.D. 627–644) were general official examinations established throughout the Middle Kingdom. Receiving all preliminary training at home under a tutor, or in a small private school, a student was permitted to present himself to the District Magistrate for the first examination only when his individual teacher considered preparation complete and his native community set the seal of approval on his character.

If the candidate's work proved satisfactory, the District Magistrate passed the young man on to the Prefect for further testing, and that dignitary in turn to the Emperor's special examiner. The reward of success was the *Hsu Tsai*, or first degree, approximately equivalent to a Western A.B. Announcement of this honor was posted on the doorway of the recipient's home to inform the world that under this roof dwelt one of the *literati*, who was eligible for government office and exempt from common demands of public service, as well as from corporal punishment, should he run afoul of the Law.

He received, also, an immediate increase in respect from all his contemporaries, but when one considers the responsibility which now settled on the shoulders of the young first-degree man, such honors and privileges seem poor compensation. Personal ambition, family prestige, and hope for desirable appointment, all now combined to mold his life along serious, studious lines. His future must be a continuous preparation for higher degrees with their increasingly difficult examination requirements, and should he, in the course

萬般皆下品惟有讀書高古詩

萬般皆下品惟有讀書高古詩

of time, have the superlative fortune to become a candidate for highest honors, his testing would then come from the Emperor, himself. One inescapable qualification for advancement was that of unsullied reputation, and when official appointment was finally received, even that hard-earned reward would be tinged with the bitterness of exile, for custom demanded that he serve not among his own people, but in some distant province, where there would be no temptation to use office for the benefit of relatives and friends.

It is not strange that men who lived this severe, disciplinary existence of passing from one "Forest of Pens," as the Chinese called the Examination Halls, to another should occasionally have sacrificed integrity for swifter material returns, but for the most part the old Chinese system developed officials who accepted their responsibilities gravely. The very fact that positions of power were the result of individual capacity and not of inheritance made a democratic bond between officialdom and common people. While the ordinary citizen respected highly the brains and ability that had lifted these others in authority over him, he never for one moment considered them on an equal plane with that Son of Heaven who ruled from the Dragon Throne. Officials and citizenry were of the same clay, and the man in the street realized sensibly that but for a turn of Fortune's Wheel, he, himself, might be occupying an official residence.

Because of this kinship, the governed was aware also that in his hands lay the power to depose any imperial representative who became too derelict in duty or too flagrantly evil in private life. For the same reason, perhaps, he advocated such a course rarely, admitting with typical racial tolerance that, were he beset by the official's temptations, he might do even worse. Accordingly, the *Ta Lao Yeh*, or Great Old Ear, as the official was expressively called, seldom forgot completely the source from which he had sprung, and Chinese history is rich with names of wise ministers who braved their sovereigns' anger to preserve the people's rights.

Whatever modernists may claim concerning the stultifying limitations of Classical Learning, they cannot say that it failed to imbue courage in its adherents, for through the ages, Chinese scholars have seemed to consider life itself a small gambit where principles and convictions were involved. Certainly, no more inspiring record of behavior exists in world history than that of China's *literati* when Tsin Hsi Hwang-ti burned the books in 213 B.C. That supremely ambitious ruler, finding will and action thwarted at every turn by scholars' references to the accepted ways of good sovereigns in the historical records, took what he considered

萬般皆下品惟有讀書高
古詩

萬般皆下品惟有讀書高古詩

the most direct means of ending opposition; namely, by offering its proponents the alternatives of destroying these books that were so inimical to him, or of facing death. They chose the latter and thousands accepted with composure and fortitude the fate of being buried alive, or even more dreadful, of being condemned to torturing labor on the Great Wall. This destruction failed in its purpose, for within a generation or so there was a resurrection of the volumes which persecuted owners had managed before arrest to hide, and Ancient Learning became once more the most powerful factor in the life of the Empire.

Neither martyrs nor high officials, however, constitute a norm for China's literary class since the great majority of scholars throughout the centuries were men who failed to acquire the first degree, or having been awarded it, never reached higher ground. From the standpoint of the elect, these others sank into swift oblivion as poorly paid teachers and scribes with all hope of career ended, but in their home spheres the so-called "failures" possessed tremendous influence. There they were accepted as men learned in history, art, and literature; qualified to instruct others; to arbitrate in disputes, and to shape the communal pattern of individual behavior. Usually these less fortunate scholars possessed little of material bounty, but when they walked abroad, men greeted their approach with lowered voices and more careful speech; and farmers, merchants, and artisans seeking advice in personal problems, soon wore a pathway to their doors.

The very gravity of Confucian studies sobered and aged these young scholars beyond their years and constant meditation on the good and the beautiful lent even the most shallow-spirited among them a dignity of carriage and an austerity of expression that impelled respect. Classical Learning, limited though it was to a few cultural subjects, required from an educated man that he be freely familiar with all phases of national history, philosophical movements, art, and literature; that he express himself not only acceptably but beautifully in the two mediums of speech, poetry and prose; and that his life be conducted ethically and with propriety. It neglected the sciences; refused stubbornly to face a changing and rapidly expanding world; and gave no slightest attention to means of making a living. Instead, the chief end and aim of a lifetime of study in China seems to have been the simple matter of learning how to live.

In time scholars' faces, like those of other men, became the books on which thought left its imprint; that most of these expressed tolerance, integrity, and kindliness is a fine tribute to the sources that fed their

萬般皆下品惟有讀書高 古詩

萬般皆下品惟有讀書高 古詩

minds. "The princely man stoops to nothing that is low or unworthy; his conduct is affection and benevolence in operation; he is never satisfied with himself"—these were the basic tenets of the Confucian creed and on this foundation students strove to build life's structure.

The chief character of *An Old Scholar Remembers* is typical of this great class of honorable, dignified, and mild-mannered men. Patience in adversity, endurance in suffering, composure under persecution—these have long been their common attributes, and T'sen Scholar, though that was not his real name, could say with Wen Tien-hsiang, "There is that within me which no misfortune can steal away."

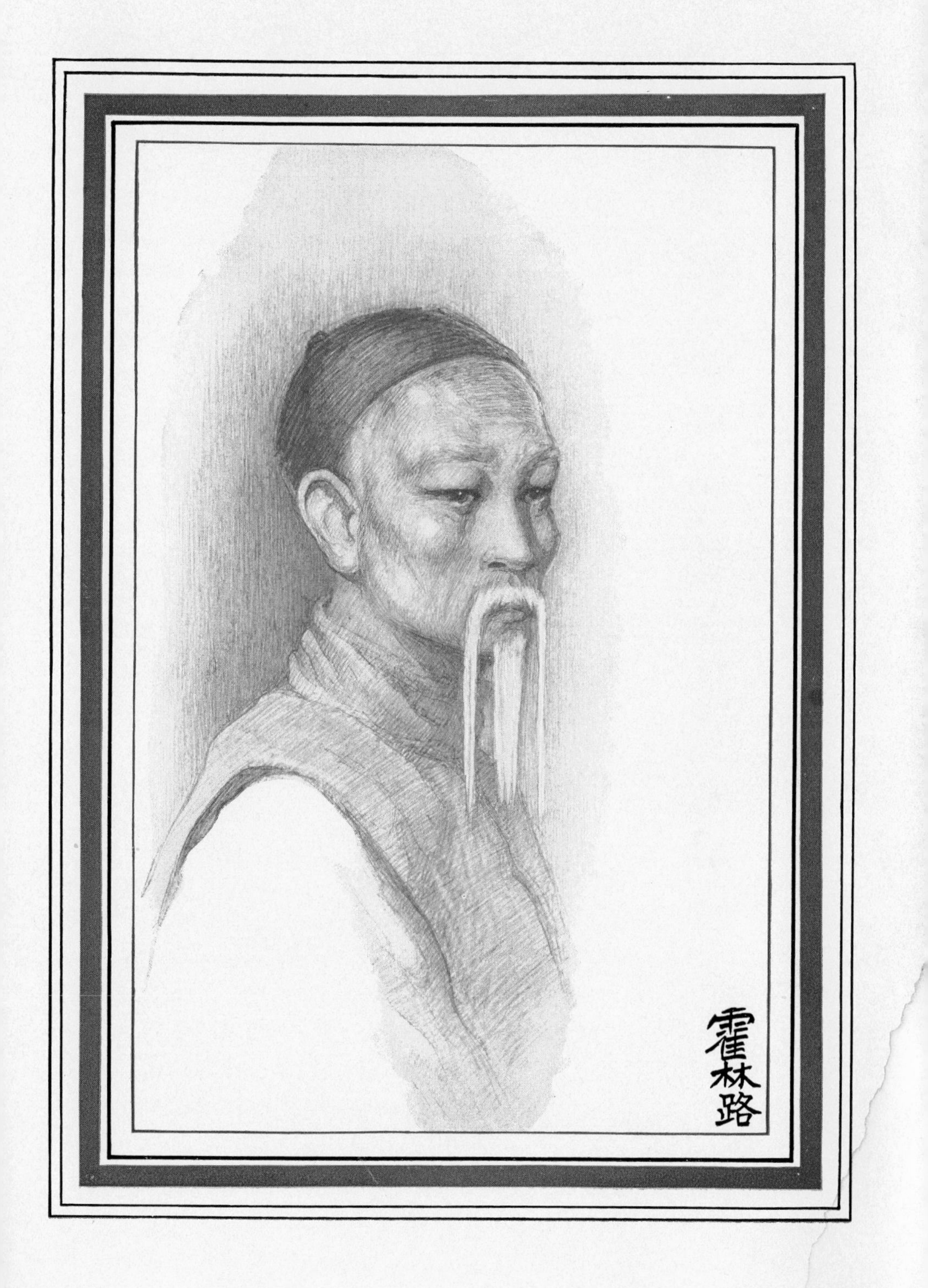
霍林路

AN OLD SCHOLAR REMEMBERS

I

The gray stone wall surrounding the house overlooked the river's bank. Midway in the masonry stood a tall, wooden gate, reinforced by stout bars and locks and well fitted to exclude marauders or other undesired guests. Along the top of the enclosure, pieces of glass and sharp bamboo were imbedded in the clay for the same purpose. These gave the place with its exposed location an appearance of much needed protection and privacy, for here, on the road that passed the gate, the city walked. Elaborate automobiles and carriages holding the wealthy crowded the wheelbarrows and rickshas on which traveled citizens of a poorer class with their belongings. Food vendors tapped gongs and offered steaming dishes for sale; load-coolies swung burdens from shoulder poles and chanted as they paced, "*Hei ho, Hai ho*"; and horribly deformed beggars, many of whom were members of a wealthy guild, clutched at the garments of passers-by or ran after moving vehicles, shrieking their appeals for pity and a copper coin.

Just outside the half-opened, wooden gateway sat an old, scholarly figure on a square, four-legged stool. He was clothed in a long, blue cotton gown which, slit at each side from foot to knee, disclosed baggy trousers wrapped tightly around the ankles with bands of corded silk ribbon, two inches in width. Below these, socks of coarse, white cotton cloth disappeared within frayed, black satin slippers. His short jacket was buttoned high against the throat and extended only to the waist. This, of the same material as the shoes, was in even more threadbare condition.

Save for a few long, drooping hairs at each side of the mouth, the fine old face, rising above the worn collar, was beardless. On the closely shaven head fitted a gored, round, black sateen cap. This the wearer removed occasionally to run his fingers over the sparse growth on his skull. Before him a small tray rested on a box and in this were grouped packets of thin rice paper, long narrow envelopes, several brushlike pens, and a slab of dried ink.

With each hand slipped inside the shelter of the opposite sleeve and with eyes half-closed, the scholar leaned back against the stone wall and dreamed. Alone in the uproar of the busy thoroughfare he sat, a small island of silence. There was no need for him to speak; the writing material on the tray told all who passed that here was a man of some education, who could be persuaded for a few copper cash to write letters of merit and distinction, should such be desired. To seek trade was beneath the dignity of one with learning, and until some patron should request his assistance, he was free to meditate.

As was so often the case, thought retreated along a well-beaten path, to the days of youth in his native province of Szechuen. A far distant journey it was, hundreds of miles west on the treacherous Son of the Sea, to that land of fertile fields, sparkling waterways, and flanking, dark-blue mountains that moved steadfastly onward to Tibetan strongholds. Memory closed in upon him, smothering present reality as completely as if his senses had yielded to the cloying drug found in Szechuen's own broad poppy fields. In the bright morning sunlight, traffic now surged with heavy increase, but the scholar's old eyes saw none of it. Instead, lost to the moment, they strained to glimpse the shadowy wraiths of years long past, as these, one after the other, stepped from a familiar burial place to play their ghostlike parts on recollection's stage.

II

"Rumors of trouble by nightfall dart here and there as if sent from a crossbow." T'sen Elder lifted to his lips a bowl of steaming, orange-scented tea and breathed in its fragrance. Slowly he sipped the liquid, then with a slight motion of his fingers settled the lid on the dish and replaced that carefully upon the lacquered table before him. For a moment, before turning again to his son, a tall, slender man in the early twenties, he looked away to the low mountains which hemmed in the surrounding country. "As though from a crossbow," he repeated, "and perhaps with as good aim!"

"But, is it not true, Sir, that this time Szechuen has little to fear?" asked his companion hopefully. "I have heard that Kweichow troops cannot hope to cross our borders, so strong at present is the defense."

The older man smiled cynically. "Confidence about strife flourishes only in the soil of youthful inexperience. Age knows better than to predict how or when any conflict once started will end. War is a madness squeezing mercy and tolerance from men, until their minds and hearts become as dry as yesterday's sucked orange lying in the sun. Szechuen has no more quarrel with Kweichow than with far-off Fukien or Chihli, but because two *tuchuns* wish further honors and loot, the rest of us face disaster." He paused briefly to drink again, then resumed bleakly, "Always the men of our class pay most: the poor having little, lose little, and a mud hut is easy to rebuild. Due to ambitious militarists in this province, our family fortune has become through recent generations but as a mustard seed to what it once was. And the losses of silver have been trivial compared with others our ancestors have endured."

He arose, an imposing figure, to look through the doorway of the summerhouse. Beyond the garden, now aflame with bloom, shimmering waves of heat wove a crazy tapestry of light and shade over the countryside. At the foot of the hill terraced rice fields gleamed like small, green glacier lakes, and past them ran an old flagstone road, about five feet wide. On this highway of history most of the travel between Kweichow and Szechuen streamed, and in the event of war, Kweichow's troops might once more darken it to oblivion. *In the event of war,* T'sen Senior repeated to himself. There was unrest, greater than usual, throughout the province. Heat had come, and with it the stirring of men's passions for change and excitement. "I go now," he said with a glance of affection for his son. "As for you, return to the Classics and thank High Heaven for books as a refuge from the follies and stupidities of men." Turning, he clasped hands behind him and walked slowly in the direction of the house.

Through the drowsy hours of early afternoon, the young man remained at his studies in the summerhouse, concentrating with difficulty on material which would be an important part of his first official examination. Until now he had worried little about this prospect of war between the two provinces, but that his father felt more gravely concerned than usual was evident. True, their home lay in the direct line of march to Chungking, which as wealthy port city would be the natural objective of the Kweichow troops, should these succeed in crossing the Szechuen border.

Abruptly he closed the volumes before him, strode outside, and glanced across countryside and river to where Chungking rose on its heights. At present, people crowded the banks like bustling ants, hurrying to and fro in the usual activities of daily living, but by sunset when summer evening mist began spreading upward from the Yangtze and its smaller confluent, the Lin, rumors of war would leave deserted, save for an occasional outcast so badly afflicted or diseased that danger held no further terrors, these same teeming slopes between the water and the city walls.

Already, here on the hills wealthy landowners had barricaded gateways and armed retainers with knives or farming implements to be used in emergency, then buried their most valuable possessions where looting soldiers would be least likely to discover such objects. Aside from these simple precautions, however, the rural sections could expect no protection, for the Szechuenese war lords concentrating their chief strength around Chungking had, contrary to general belief, stationed a wholly inadequate line of defense on the road that ran south from the Yangtze Kiang to the Kweichow border.

Under the T'sen roof the approach of night was attended by unusual activity. To the head of the house, smoking quietly in the reception hall, fragments of excited speech from the courts drifted in, punctuating thought at illogical intervals into a disconnected succession of phrases. Here in the room with him, his two grown sons moved about restlessly. Glancing from the older, more settled man to the younger who earlier that day in the summerhouse had seemed undisturbed by the threat of war, he inquired gravely, "Can you not wait patiently for that which is to come? At present your minds are swayed like rice plants in a summer storm. Fear is to be expected in the women's quarters, but for men of this family to squeeze heart in hand at such moments, is strange indeed!"

"Would that some word might come from the border!" exclaimed the elder son defensively, pulling a fan from his sleeve and shaking loose its folds. For a half-dozen strokes the object stirred the air, then was returned abruptly to its hiding place.

"Such knowledge," his father reminded him, "is written on a scroll not yet untied for reading; lacking certainty—why fear the worst? Life is a temporary loan at best and the Wheel on which it turns is always just, beyond man's power to control. *Muh iu fa tz!*"

In response the other seated himself slowly, but the younger brother, standing beside a lotus-shaped grill in the wall, continued to stare out into the darkness. Through this casement, moisture choked by overhanging cliffs as it rose from the river bosoms sifted to him in thin, clammy breaths. Mist always cloaked the countryside at dusk, but tonight the atmosphere seemed imbued with a quality sinisterly capable of concealing any danger within its enveloping folds.

The very quiet of these lonely hills accented fear and served as sharp contrast to what the young man realized was occurring within Chungking's gray stone walls. Long before this the last of the riverbank colony had sought sanctuary inside the city gates where, homeless and undesired, they added to the confusion of a citizenry wretchedly engrossed in preparation for hasty flight should that later prove necessary. On ancient barricades encircling the heights, sentries, their rifle barrels pushed through loopholes, strained eyes to pierce the fog in search of suspicious craft on the water below, for Chungking's chief arteries of life, her rivers, were on the occasion of war with the South, the potential avenues of greatest danger.

To reach these, the man at the casement reminded himself with a chill prickling of skin, the enemy must first sweep past his own gateway, and should they decide to enter, what defense could he and his family offer? A few knives, two long swords, and an antiquated rifle hidden beneath the heavy carved chest on which his brother now sat were their only weapons with which to meet well-equipped troops. Slowly he shrugged the disquieting thoughts from him. As his father had said, "*Muh iu fa tz!*" All one could do was to wait.

Suspense chained Night's lagging footsteps, and like aged refugees bent under the burden of fear, the minutes hobbled by with painful slowness. Not until the Hour of the Ox had come, bringing with it prospect of dawn and the hope of avoided conflict, did the blow fall. In a sudden wave of running feet, splintering wood, and raucous shouts, clamor washed over the hills. Terrified, the gateman rushed into the hall crying, "Masters, already several tens of soldiers force our gate. What can we do?" The question ended with a thin scream of pain as a sword thrust in the old servant's back felled him where he stood, and over his body armed men swarmed into the quiet, beautiful room.

III

To the younger son, lying half-conscious beneath a clump of bamboos, there came the sound of beating drums. No, not drums—carpenters hammering! What queer rhythm there was to the work! Drowsily his clouded mind considered this peculiarity, then with growing clarity recognized the staccato explosions for what they really were. Somewhere in the distance troops were engaged in battle, and vague questions now began to shape themselves among his thoughts. Reassured by the quiet peace about him, he attempted feebly to dismiss these disturbing intruders. The conflict, wherever it was, held no personal interest for him and his rest might continue for a while. Why was there particular need for him to rest? he wondered, then became aware of throbbing head pain. Experimenting with strength, he lifted eyelids and with difficulty focused his gaze on slender branches curving above him. How did he happen to be in the garden? After several efforts, when consciousness was engulfed by successive waves of blackness, he managed to raise himself on one elbow and to recognize a few yards away the dwelling place which had belonged to the T'sen family for generations. His puzzled gaze now discovered that the pongee garment clothing him was badly stained and torn, then without further warning, memory buffeted him mercilessly into complete consciousness.

The entry of the soldiers—was it last night? the wounded man asked himself—had been followed by a clash involving the entire household. He could recall firing to advantage the old rifle snatched from beneath the chest, and later using it desperately as a club to batter a way toward his father. As he reached the other's side, a knife flashed above the older man, then plunged, and the son brought the barrel of his weapon down murderously on the assailant's head. Beyond that act nothing seemed clear to him now and no further effort should be wasted in trying to recreate the scene. Instead, he crawled slowly to his feet and staggered in the direction of the house.

On the threshold of the reception room the wounded man stumbled over the still, crumpled body of a servant. The shock of this made him retch agonizingly. After a little while, clutching the doorframe for support, he forced himself to look farther into the room. There, terrifyingly still, sprawled several other figures, but his father's, he soon saw, was not among them. Hope surged within him that this parent lived, and with other survivors might be hiding on these very grounds. Huskily he called out several times; his own voice echoing faintly in the silent rooms was the only response. Was it likely, Good Judgment argued, it his family had found safety close by, that he, the younger son, would have been left to his fate here in the garden? A sense of desolation added itself now to physical exhaustion and he sank slowly to the sill.

An hour or two later, midday sun beating on his face woke him once more. In his ears continued the monotonous sound of shots. Between these reports he listened again for some sign of life about the place. Certainly all of this great household had not died. Where then had they fled for refuge? To Chungking? He dismissed this idea at once, aware that the battle now raging was probably around Chungking. Under the brilliant sunlight his eyelids closed down upon vision like hot metallic discs, and he clung greedily to the desire for sleep. When, after several defeats, his mind finally conquered physical demands, he struggled again to stand. A search of the premises revealed nothing further and, with maturing decision, he turned and followed a narrow path between two bean fields. In time, this would lead him to a hut on the Yangtze's shore, some distance below the main crossing to Chungking. There he hoped to find the servant who acted as boatman for the estate and to learn from him, or from someone under his roof, whether or not any of the T'sen family had sought escape by river.

In the noontide heat, the two *li* of distance to the river seemed an interminable avenue of suffering for the lonely pedestrian. Feet responded unsteadily to the brain's commands, and with each fresh wave of pain, his head seemed to expand and contract. Liquid trickled down a cheek, and when exploring fingers lifted to his scalp came away red, faintness seized him once more. He sat down at the edge of a field to rest before going on.

The quiet, smothering depths into which he had sunk changed now to an atmosphere of coolness and the pleasantly regular swish of water against a hull. Lying bound on the deck of a ship that slid smoothly along with the current, the young man breathed in the refreshing air gratefully and wondered why, having set out to find and question the family boatman, he should have ended in his present surroundings. This vessel was certainly no sampan for ferrying purposes, but a stout river craft; moreover, his ankles and wrists were tied securely, and unless he had fallen again into the hands of soldiers, this development seemed hard to understand.

Ceilinged by the figured velvet of a starry sky, perpendicular cliffs rose high on either shore, further assuring him that this was not the familiar, broad stretch of river at Chungking. His eyes, now accustomed to the dark, blinked painfully when a stocky figure carrying a lantern appeared and bent over him.

"So," exclaimed the newcomer in broad Hupeh dialect, "you do live, is it not true? I thought I had spent time and strength uselessly, but after food and rest, you will yet repay me for my trouble."

Even more puzzled by these remarks, the young man moved parched lips. "You speak as my benefactor—wherefore, then, these bonds?"

The *Lao Dah* shouted his amusement. "Benefactor, am I? Lao Ching," he called to a servant, "come here! This fellow has waked and calls me his benefactor. *Ai-ya*, he speaks laugh-talk!" Turning again to the captive, he added, "Yes, your good friend, even your honey friend am I! Of a certainty you would have died had we left you in the sun of that field. A humble man am I, but full of good deeds—you, yourself, have said it—poverty alone makes me ask friends to help earn my living. Is it not so, Lao Ching?"

With mock solemnity the servant agreed, "*Shi, shi, Lao Dah!*"

After a moment the captain resumed his bantering, "You are traveling to Ichang and the trip will cost you nothing. Moreover. until we reach that port, I ask none of your services. Several days of journeying remain, so mend your strength and enjoy the scenery, Honorable Hsien-Seng, remembering that many men would envy you this chance to see the gorges."

Cold with fear, the young man asked, "When we come to Ichang—then what?"

"You seem hasty for one of your class," came reprovingly, "but the young are always impatient, whether scholars or something else. Now listen: except for your broken head you have strength, and doubtless, in a short time will be able to pull and climb with the best of them. In the future living will be very simple; you will have no use for silk garments and satin shoes—a loincloth and straw sandals will be enough—indeed, too much, when wading or swimming. Trackers' needs are few."

With a drop of the eyelids, the prisoner shut himself in with this bitter disclosure. A tracker he was to become—his body, like any beast at man's command, to be forced into pulling vessels over the rapids and whirlpools of this Upper Yangtze when neither sails nor oars were of use. Was it only a day or two ago that he had pored over learned volumes in preparation for an official career? Then life had been rich with family and friends; suddenly none of these possessions remained and he, himself, was a captive doomed to the worst that could befall any man. How he had fallen into their hands gradually became clear. Sitting down to rest that last time, he must have been close to the water's edge and these river pirates, always on the lookout for prey, had found him senseless and an easy victim to their designs.

After the captain had walked away, Lao Ching unbound the prisoner, then brought steaming rice and tea. Grasping the tea bowl, the young man pushed the food from him.

"Eat and get strength, or you will be worth little to us!" the servant ordered brusquely, pushing forward the food bowl and *kwai-tz*.

When the other had departed, the young man still made no effort to eat. Why not throw the contents into the river, his tortured thoughts demanded, while his captors were not watching? Starvation, added to wound and shock, might soon kill him, and suicide seemed the only solution left him. As he lifted the bowl to the rail, his father's voice echoed in his ears: "Compose your spirit! At present, you are like rice swayed in a summer storm; wait patiently for that which is to come. For men of this family to squeeze heart in hand at the approach of danger is strange indeed!" Wearily the young man lowered the bowl, then adjusting the *kwai-tz* between his fingers, began to eat.

In the days that followed, strength returned rapidly, a fact which he hid from his captors by pretending sleep and weakness. It would not do to have them realize that his value to them was increasing daily. It was apparent that he was the only victim of this sort aboard and the peculiarly sweet odor of opium soon informed him that the *Lao Dah's* chief income came from smuggling drugs and not men. As the wound in his head healed and pain ceased, he began to plan for escape.

Lying in a *pu-gai* on the deck, he watched the swirling water, just below, stretch out hungry fingers toward this boat as to all others. Great junks were beached everywhere along the shores, their salvaged cargoes spread in the sun to dry. On one occasion screams called his horrified attention to a small fishing craft which, circling faster and ever faster until it stood on end in a whirlpool, disappeared with the crew from the eyes of men forever. A moment earlier, the victims chanted in the sunlight; the next, they were gone. Once more the River Dragon had taken toll and where was the man who, realizing that his turn might come next, would dare to offer resistance or criticism? Small wonder that among the shrieking winds and menacing rocks of these Upper River Gorges mariners held no doubts of the demon's power.

Two dawns later they anchored off Ichang, completing in six days from Chungking a journey which going upstream would require from four to eight weeks. In midmorning, the *Lao Dah*, accompanied by another crafty-looking individual, walked toward the prisoner. With eyes half-closed the latter feigned sleep, until a well-directed kick from Lao Ching and the order, "Stand up!" forced him into action. Groaning and swaying dizzily, he arose. The ruse worked, for the stranger, grasping the young man's arm muscles, gave the captain a disgusted look. "Why waste my time on sick men?" he demanded and strode away.

Arguing hotly and cursing between breaths, the captain followed the angry visitor from the boat. In the afternoon he returned with another prospective customer. This one was hurried. He looked the young man over hastily and said, "All right, I'll send for him at daybreak."

The *Lao Dah* scowled. "Take him with you now! The price is low and does not include evening rice."

"Tonight, I have no use for him. In the morning at the Hour of the Hare, he comes, or not at all. Many such may be had, and for tracking, your man is a poor bargain. I agreed only because my affairs are many, and the hours before leaving, few. Therefore—!" the speaker shrugged shoulders, then, without further ado, started toward the gunwale, where the sampan in which he had come bobbed on the current.

Not until the captain saw this customer step into the smaller boat did he start forward, and with a twisted smile, acquiesce. "Suit yourself—it is unimportant! He stays here until the Hour of the Hare, but eats no morning rice."

Spreading hands in a gesture of approval, the purchaser turned back. In a few moments, papers and money were exchanged, the transaction completed, and the *Lao Dah* once more accompanied a visitor ashore.

Unless he succeeded in escaping tonight, his services now belonged to this stranger of many affairs, thought the young man desperately. So far, the boat's crew had paid him little attention; Lao Ching, alone, had been on constant watch and he felt that his one chance of escape would be to slip away while this guardian was eating evening food and the captain was still ashore. For his silk garments the *Lao Dah* had given him jacket and pants of blue cotton coolie cloth, and wearing these the prisoner resembled, at a distance, any one of a thousand other figures on these boats.

Dusk came on and small, flickering lights appeared, deepening the darkness. At the other end of the craft, the crew sat around a charcoal fire where food was being prepared. A succession of houseboats crowded close to this one, and their decks might be used as steppingstones to safety. Such a course would present no difficulty; houseboat crews were accustomed to strangers passing to and fro and asked no questions. This was his one chance, for they were anchored in deep water and he could swim only a few strokes.

He had played his part well these days, and the captain, thinking him a weakling and a fool, had not troubled to renew the bonds here in port. His heart was pounding. Through the smoke of the charcoal fire, he could see Lao Ching squatting with a bowl of rice. Noiselessly the captive arose, and gauging distance as well as was possible in the dark, stepped on the adjoining houseboat's deck. There he leaned breathless in the shadow of a cabin and waited to see if Lao Ching or the others had noticed the sudden swaying of the boat as his shifted weight released it. When no sound came to him except the clicking of *kwai-tz* and the smacking of lips, he turned his back and moved over to the next boat. Continuing this procedure cautiously, he soon had a dozen decks between him and his own.

For a moment the young man paused. His one idea was to land and flee into the country. With this much start to his advantage they could hardly hope to find him; and the *Lao Dah*, lawbreaker that he was, would not dare to call on the police for assistance in recovering a victim of his own piracy. None of these houseboats were close to shore, but crossing to still another craft, he saw beside it that which seemed beyond hope—a sampan, its small lantern fastened to a pole and swaying with the current. Oars drawn, there was no sign of life about it until he called.

A sleepy voice answered, "*La-ih-ko?*"

"A passenger who wishes to go ashore!"

"How much will you pay?"

"I have no silver, but here is a pair of new straw sandals in exchange."

"Straw shoes can be bought for a few cash; to row passengers in these swift waters is worth a dime, big money."

A dime! He had nothing else save the two cotton garments on his body. Any minute, however, they might begin to search for him. "My jacket you may have," he called, and the rower, after consideration, accepted.

"Quickly!" the young man ordered as he stepped aboard, but the other did not stir.

"There is a passenger, whom I carried from the city to this houseboat beside us. When he wishes to return, we go."

The listener's hands clenched in fear; every second of waiting here meant added time for Lao Ching to discover his absence. He looked about him; no other sampan was in sight. *Mu iu fa tz!* He was in the hands of the gods.

What seemed like hours to him were, in reality, a few minutes. Two men walked out on the boat deck and came toward the smaller craft. They bowed farewell, then one, stepping down beside the young man, noticed the silent figure and asked curiously, "Who is this?"

The rower, busy about untying, mumbled, "Another who wishes to go ashore!"

To the escaping prisoner, there came a shivering sensation of peril. Where had he heard this voice before? Loosened, the little boat swayed suddenly and the lantern light fell full on the faces of the two passengers. At the same instant, they recognized each other. So misfortune was still amusing itself with him! thought the younger of the two, overwhelmed by this fresh calamity of facing his new master. For a moment only he hesitated, then with one leap was in the river.

The rower stared, but the other wasted no time on surprise. "Catch him!" he ordered sharply.

In the dim light of the lantern the searchers found it difficult to distinguish the dark head from the blackness of night and water. Frantic over the likelihood of losing that for which he had already bargained, the new owner flung the long-poled boat hook over the side and striking out blindly, caught in something solid. In a few moments with the protesting boatman's help the quarry had been pulled aboard and bound.

Pushing the sampan toward the shore, the rower continued to mutter his fears about having cheated the river. His chief passenger shivered, then exclaimed, "Not so; it was my right! He is a tracker for whose services I had paid in advance."

"Wonderful, indeed!" remarked the other shrewdly. "Since when did trackers learn to talk and act like scholars? I did not arrive on earth, yesterday."

The *Lao Dah* turned on him hotly, "Is this your affair?"

"It is not mine, Most Honorable Captain," came the reply, and the trip was completed in silence.

Next morning, when the young man peered about his dimly lighted surroundings, he found himself in the hold of what seemed to be a large junk. The rags on which he lay smelt of the river, and a gently rocking motion convinced him he was not on land. Voices mingled with the sounds of grating ropes and settling baggage, and shortly afterwards the vessel shuddered, heaved upward, then found its depth again with a thud. They had cast off.

Men rushed up and down the ladder that led to the darkened hold, but paid no attention to its lone occupant. Finally, an old fellow issuing directions about bales of Peiping furs, finished, approached the prisoner, silently unbound him and motioned him to follow. They climbed the narrow ladder, went down a dark passageway, up another ladder, and out on a deck crowded by men.

There the new arrival, left for the time to his own devices, began to study his companions, who were the trackers for this trip. Dirt, rags, and matted hair were their common possession. One busily searched the seams of his jacket for lice; another packed a pill of opium into a pipe for later use; all eagerly awaited midday food. Presently it was brought to them—coarse rice and inferior tea. That, in spite of their wretched condition, these men could joke and laugh as they ate amazed the onlooker. He turned away from his own unappetizing portion of the meal in disgust, but hunger reminded him that he had eaten nothing since noon the preceding day, and in a little time, his two bowls were emptied.

Hours passed slowly; the wind was with the sails and the trackers were called upon to do nothing. At night, they anchored in a quiet cove. His companions gambled the darkness away, their incessant arguments making sleep fitful for others. When the first faint strips of gray lightened the night sky, the junk moved onward. Soon, the narrowing current grew more swift, and one of the crew testing carefully the heavy coils of bamboo hawser set the trackers to straightening out individual lines. These, ending in slip loops, had knots placed at various intervals to halt sliding hands. Ropes in readiness, the trackers now awaited action as a seething, white line appeared on the surface upstream. A boat was lowered and the men bearing the hawsers that connected them to the ship rowed rapidly to shallows along the shore and jumped overboard.

The boiling wall of water came closer, and in response to a curt order the trackers heaved forward with their burden. Muscles strained to the snapping point; blood pounded in temples; but, inch by inch, they pulled the junk up to the foaming rapid. Twice, their burden refused to meet the flood; twice, the men fell back many yards, stumbling, slipping, upsetting each other in a mad effort to pay out the ropes. At the last of the lines a slender novice, his breath coming in painfully short gasps, struggled at the unfamiliar task of holding his line. Once more the trackers, small forms of agonizing energy pitting their strength against an elemental foe, steadied to action. Again came the signal to advance; this time the ship rose, shivered from bow to stern, pushed upward, and settled her keel in the placid stretch at the head of the rapids. The men now caught up lines and began to scramble aboard, but the inexperienced one, noosed in a suddenly slackening hawser and, unable to extricate himself, was thrown into the river and there washed free of his bonds. Floating downstream, he landed on a spit of beach and lay there exhausted waiting for authority to force him again into service. Gradually all sound of human activity faded in the roar of the rapids, and the young man began to wonder what strange miracle had occurred to permit so prolonged a respite. When at last he dared to risk discovery by sitting up, the junk had already disappeared around a curving wall of rock, and assurance increased that the crew, having so far failed to note his absence, would later on merely count him a part of the River Dragon's toll and make no effort at further search.

His first decision was to place distance between himself and the river. Above him in an apparently unbroken wall rose the great, silent cliff. No living thing stirred. He stood up, wrung water from his garments, and began to explore the narrow strip of shore. After a while he came to a jutting contour of rock that sloped down to the beach much like an animal leaning to drink, and upon climbing around this, he discovered a sharp division in the stony surface. Hardly wider than a man's shoulders, at first sight the aperture seemed impassable, but staring through this natural cleavage, the searcher became aware of an opening at the other end.

His hands and feet, already bruised and torn, found progress along this path painfully slow. Midway a small, dark, velvety form hanging upside down in a stony niche fluttered from beneath his fingers and swooped blindly into deeper shadows. For the first time since the Kweichow troops had descended on his home, the young man knew a lifting of spirit. Bats were always good omens and perhaps this tiny creature might symbolize a change in fortune for himself. Encouraged, he quickened progress, and after a time emerged on a meadowland of grass and wild flowers.

There he paused to rest and plan. The sun was already high in a cloudless sky and food and shelter must be found before dark. Near by was no sign of habitation other than a wisp of smoke which penciled itself against the blue horizon, far to the southeast. Fire undoubtedly meant a settlement and that should be his destination. He stooped and gathered leaves and straw with which to bind his sore feet; then picking up a rotted tree branch, he broke away the decayed section and started across the fields.

Securing sustenance was the first problem and, since starvation seemed preferable to begging, he began to wonder what hidden talents might be his to use. After a little, the idea came to pass himself off as an itinerant storyteller. This was an attraction few country people could resist, and even in so great a city as Chungking, these entertainers found no difficulty in drawing crowds about them. His own dramatic ability had never before been tested; moreover, as a scholar, he was unfamiliar with the romantic novels which were part of every storyteller's stock in trade but certainly no one in the profession was better acquainted with historical tales than himself. His chief handicaps were these cotton garments and a bedraggled condition; however, the simple statement of having been attacked and robbed would serve to explain his appearance.

The settlement proved to be a village of twenty or thirty mud huts, with one built in better fashion of wood and plaster. As expected, this was the inn, and, using his stick to push away the snapping curs that pressed like wolves about him, he entered and sat down at one of the tables.

The *Lao Ban* exchanged greetings, then eyed this disreputable-looking stranger suspiciously. "What do you wish?" he asked.

The young man smiled, "To make a bargain with you."

"Just as I feared!" came the reply. "Hear me: I make bargains in terms of food and cash only."

"Food I wish; cash I lack, Honorable *Lao Ban!* It is easy for me to see that for a man of your intelligence explanations are unnecessary; nevertheless, I shall tell you that I am a storyteller who, in traveling this way, had the great misfortune to be set upon by brigands. They took all that I had, and in exchange left me these poor garments and nothing else." As he talked, he found his tongue becoming fluent in this role of unfortunate traveler and he continued with ease. "Now one must live, and if it suits your convenience, I shall stand in front of your important establishment and bring you more patrons than you have had in many a day. This will I do in exchange for rice and tea. The tea I must have, at once—dry throats are of no use in my business; the rice, when I have finished. If by that time, you do not think that I have earned a bowlful, you are at liberty to refuse it."

The innkeeper's eyes, frowning upon this puzzling customer, showed sudden interest. A storyteller—yes, that might bring some trade from his neighbors on an afternoon void of travelers, he thought to himself, then agreed openly, "It shall be as you have said." Later, having drunk his bowl of tea, the young man stationed himself at the entrance to the inn and began to talk.

IV

The old scholar opened his eyes and became aware once more of the busy thoroughfare. An eight-year-old with shaven scalp, in the center of which one patch of black hair stood erect, bent over the writing materials on the tray.

"Look, but do not touch!" the owner cautioned gently.

"A thousand pardons, Honorable Teacher," apologized the boy, bowing his head toward the ground three times, "I meant no harm."

The wise old eyes lighted with warmth. Unlike many of his generation, this street urchin had been taught courteous ways at least. "Would you like to write characters?" the scholar inquired gravely.

"Very much, Revered Sir! I wish to write words and read books and perhaps, when I am old, become a great man like you. In our family, though, there is not enough money for food, so of course, none for learning."

Here was a child hungry to do books and denied the opportunity! For a moment the elderly figure remained silent and immobile, then with a sudden impulse addressed the would-be student. "Son of Wise Fathers, what is your excellent name?"

"Those under my miserable and dishonorable roof are called Lu, Great Teacher, and I, the third son, am Hsiao San."

Moistening his ink tablet, the scholar took up a brush, shaped it to a hairlike point, and began to write.

"Stand at my left, Young Seeker of Wisdom," he ordered, "and I will show you how to write your name. This short stroke down, then cut with a dash; form next a wide bridge and bring it to rest on one long, curving support at the left: 广 Now, close under the bridge, a smaller curve which follows the right and is cleft through its middle by a sharp knife—so: 乂 ! Beneath this begin the *Tien-tz:* down, over and down, bar carefully the window and fasten: 田 ! There remains yet the *Min-tz*, a cage on a firm base 皿 , and now we have completed the good character,

Lu 盧. Cherish your name in honor! Remember always the order of the strokes, for without order, balance and beauty can be built neither in writing nor in life. Now having seen, can you write the word for me? Hold your pen with firmness and dampen it again! First the straight stroke, then the dash!"

The boy's hand grasped the brush; stiffly and crudely the *Lu* character was formed.

"It is five tenths good," said the teacher. "You have eyes that see. Only a few small errors have been made, and in the beginning, all things are difficult. Learn your first saying from the Ancient Wisdom: 'If a man study all his days, he will not know everything'."

The child, his bright, black eyes burning with eagerness, repeated the proverb carefully, word by word, and the old scholar smiled approval. "Now go, New Student, to your parents! Tell them that if it be their wish, I have chosen to teach you how to read and write. When they do not need you, and you see me with no other affairs, come to me here."

Overwhelmed by Good Fortune, the boy stared, endeavoring to control the quivering of a childishly rounded chin. When this was accomplished, he stammered, "But, Honorable Hsien-Seng, I am most unworthy of such great kindness, most unworthy!" He stooped suddenly and touched his forehead in the dust; then bowing himself away from this important presence, turned at the end of the street and ran wildly home to share the news with his mother.

The old man sighed whimsically and looked at the busy crowd going by. The child had called him "a great man." "A great man!" He tied the threads of memory which had frayed when the boy aroused him and thought again of the long, trying years between that first storytelling and today. Tramping from village to village; earning food and a few cash; searching for a more dignified and less distasteful means of livelihood; journeying ever farther from his own beautiful Szechuen! His first purchase after food had been stationery and a stamp, but having no address of more than a day's length, he had held the letter until reaching a large town, where living for a month might be found. There he had waited many days after the month had ended, but no reply had come. Again and again, he had written, and even now with all the time between, the old man could still feel those hopelessly bitter stings of disappointment when the mails failed to bring a reply. Finally, believing all in his family dead, he had given up trying to communicate with them by post and had devoted his time and strength to eking out an existence.

Down here near the coast, for a stranger, far from all who knew him, there had been no chance for anything more than that, and even though he had eventually established himself as a public letter writer on this street, he had never been able to accumulate sufficient funds to pay the long, expensive journey back to Chungking. Given another year or two of careful saving, with his old body constantly making fewer demands for food, he might yet be able to achieve this desire, provided, Common Sense reminded, that war did not interfere.

Through most of the past century his country had been tortured by almost constant warfare, sectional as well as provincial, rendering it an easy prey to a still greater conflict which now threatened from beyond the borders. Already these invaders had seized broad stretches of territory for themselves, and it was rumored that they would not stop until every foot of Chinese soil lay ground beneath their heels. He sighed. As his father had once said, no man could predict how strife when started might end, and the present government, though a good one, seemed ill-equipped to meet a united and implacable foe, for his people, accustomed through countless generations to think first of family ties, found it difficult to adopt this modern idea of spreading their loyalties over an entire nation.

He thought again of the small, shaven head, and the bright eyes that revealed a craving for knowledge. Perhaps, contrary to accepted opinion, the hope of the race lay in youths of this age instead of in elders like himself. As he had promised, he would teach this child, and some day the pupil might be able to serve his country in ways the teacher had not even imagined. But was that true? Would what he had to give help this child to meet a future which threatened to be unlike anything the Sons of Han had ever experienced? Daily more of the old ways were changing, and the young men from the universities, to whose talk he listened occasionally in a teahouse, spoke of strange studies that had to do with machines, or metals hidden in earth's bowels, or small, invisible creatures that caused disease. The subjects of these conversations were very different from those which for many centuries had occupied the attention of educated Chinese. In *The Analects* and *The Odes*, men's interest had been centered about propriety of conduct and personal relationships to others of their kind. Perhaps in this modern day, activity rather than meditation was needed, and his people must learn to use the unfamiliar tools that an unstable and storm-ridden world now thrust upon them.

Heavily the scholar sucked in his breath; for the first time in life, he was questioning the value of the Great Learning to an individual. After a moment or two there came to him the realization that while his own path had been clouded by sorrow and hardship, the wisdom of the Classics had helped him, the lonely traveler, to a dignity and a quiet of soul that relieved the sharpness of even the worst misfortunes. If the ancient books did no more than that for this lad, the efforts of teacher and student, would still be well worth-while. Once more the old man's face settled to serenity and he sat for a time meditating on the relative values of the forces that motivated man's existence. Heaven sometimes worked to strange purpose, but in the end, the Wheel of Life was always just. Picking up a small pamphlet of T'ao Yuan Ming's poems, he read until a patron disturbed him.

習俗移人賢者不免古諺

THE FOREIGNER

Strange habits of thought and action are often tools of disaster and weapons of suicide.

"From ancient times until now, few people have been able to see with their eyes," the poet, Li Po, remarked in the eighth century concerning some of his countrymen. That a thousand years later the statement might be even more reasonably applied to men of other races in his land not even his highly developed imagination could foresee. The truth remains, however, that in four centuries of close contact with Chinese, Occidentals generally have shown less wisdom than anywhere else on the globe.

Naturally, the policy of foreign aggression during most of this period has been the chief contributing factor toward mutual misunderstanding. Commencing with the unspeakable atrocities of the Spanish and Portuguese in the sixteenth century and ending with the equally indefensible treaties of 1858 in which Britain, France, Russia, and the United States joined hands, this course of action trained the Chinese to look upon any outsider with hatred and distrust. That the aggressors, on the other hand, having gained their ends, should have continued to treat the exploited Orientals with dislike and arrogance seems comprehensible, but

習俗移人賢者不免

古諺

none the more to be condoned. Through the years, these emotional indulgences have cost the foreigner in China far more than did the early campaigns to win trade privileges and acquire territorial rights, and it is possible that a still further payment is to be demanded. At present, China, fighting valiantly to withstand her latest invaders, sees the foreigners, who have long occupied her territory to their own advantage, scurry to safety, or sit by with folded hands, and her spirit of resistance is strengthened by dreams of a future when not only the Nipponese shall be driven from her shores, but all other nationals as well.

It is true that from the beginning Europeans and Americans were handicapped in dealing with these people of the Middle Kingdom who had lived to themselves for so long that few facts about them were available. Prior to 1858, officers and seamen on English brigs, Dutch barkentines, and American clippers were the chief mediums of intercourse between the countries involved. These, with all transactions and activities restricted to a few square yards of shore line in the only ports where trading was permitted, experienced the briefest of contacts with Chinese merchants and used these superficial relationships for flights of imagination concerning the whole of Cathay and its inhabitants. Accordingly most of their generalizations about an

習俗移人賢者不免古諺

unknown people were absurd fabrications, but a gullible world accepted these as facts and even today grudgingly discards them.

When, with the opening of the Treaty Ports, foreigners settling in Chinese communities were at last given the opportunity to grasp reality, understanding still grew slowly. Proud and reserved as a race, the embittered Chinese took no steps toward meeting these interlopers halfway, and the foreigners, resenting assumption of superiority in a people they mistakenly considered inferior, and struggling with the immediate difficulties of strange speech and customs, decided that the barriers between the two races were insurmountable and made little effort to lower them. That today, a brief half century or so after these flames of ill will burned at greatest heat, much of the world is friendly to the Chinese is due entirely to those nineteenth century foreigners in eastern Asia who could "see with their eyes."

During that period, the three groups of Westerners best represented numerically on China's soil were Church, State, and Commerce. Each of these had its share of broad-visioned, clear-thinking men and women who labored to forge bonds of friendship between their own nations and this one whose guests they were by sufferance. Of the three, the Church had by far the greatest proportion, and it is indisputable that missionaries, adversely criticized though they have been, and often justly, have done more to break down the walls of misunderstanding in China than has any other force.

These individuals, in painfully small groups of twos or threes, settled down in far, lonely corners of this vast land, determined to promulgate their message of good will, regardless of what the project might cost in toll of body and spirit, and equally unconcerned by having an audience stubbornly unreceptive to new ideas in general and to those of foreign derivation in particular. Not many of these representatives of British and American education and training were equipped mentally to meet the astute Chinese, and from the Oriental viewpoint, most of them were crude and ignorant of life's amenities. In spite of these handicaps, however, the missionaries continued to stumble along the uncharted paths of this ancient, highly developed civilization, stout-heartedly facing the terrors and obstacles confronting them and gradually seeing their efforts meet with reward.

Whatever they may have lacked in dialectics and culture, these preachers, doctors, and teachers possessed, in most instances, the simple virtues of sincerity, kindliness, and sympathy. They worked arduously to acquire the language (a task most foreign business men

習俗移人賢者不免
古諺

習俗移人賢者不免古諺

refused to consider); to understand the strange and unfamiliar; and to share in the life of the people, serving them wherever and whenever opportunity was presented. After a time, the Chinese began to recognize that this group of foreigners, in spite of numerous faults and oddities, was motivated apparently by no ulterior purposes, and with this admission of confidence, was laid the first beam to bridge that ideological gap which had separated China from the rest of the world for so long.

That the individual foreigner, regardless of his business there, found residence in Cathay beset by personal difficulties was natural. Thousands of miles from home and friends, the habits and ways of life to which he had been accustomed from birth assumed a special value in this land where, superficially at least, everything seemed exactly opposite to all he had known. The aggressive soul, attempting to force theories or goods on this self-sufficient race, found himself thwarted at every turn by passive indifference to his catchwords of efficiency and progress. To his desire for swift accomplishment they presented slow-moving deliberation; to his efforts at demonstrating that a straight line is the shortest distance between two given points, they responded blandly with circumlocutions that left him mentally exhausted.

He was firmly convinced that the white race was superior to the yellow, and they were equally sure of the opposite. When he demanded that they pay respect to science and invention, they countered with an invitation for him to consider the importance of art and literature in the scheme of living. The sound of their speech echoed strangely in his ears; the inescapable odor of human refuse shocked his nose, and unusual flavors in food startled his palate. When the more sensitive among these outsiders was called upon to face the brutalities which an overcrowded civilization of necessity imposed on man and beast, he sometimes grew queer and morbid under the strain, and that so many foreigners in the early stages of residence in China managed to adapt themselves as well as they did is amazing.

Not until the individual had found his own niche in this enormous field, and racial differences had been submerged by time and mutual appreciation, did those first difficulties fall into proper perspective. Only then was it possible for the alien American or European to begin taking stock of all that had been acquired from residence among the Chinese. Many of his most valuable gains lay among the imponderables, and while life provided no scales for weighing these, he realized that in the last analysis they were of infinitely greater

習俗移人賢者不免古諺

習俗移人賢者不免古諺

value than any tangible gifts the storehouses of Eastern treasure might have offered him for his own.

In this pathological study of a foreigner, *Whom the Gods Destroy*, a young and highly impressionable woman is the chief character. That she is a missionary has no slightest bearing on the subject, save that the average mission representative is, by very nature of the work, exposed to sordidness and brutality from which most women in business or diplomatic circles are usually protected. Cases of American or European inability to become successfully adapted to life in Asia are only too numerous in all fields, although few, fortunately, result in such tragedy as that instanced here. The Orient is no place for the hypersensitive, the humorless, or the intolerant soul to find itself, and it seems regrettable, indeed, that in the selection of candidates for foreign service, business corporations and mission boards should place so little emphasis on the possession of those qualities of mind and spirit which make for emotional stability in the individual.

霍林路

WHOM THE GODS DESTROY

Strife lay so far removed from the woods porch where we sat in the late October afternoon that it seemed incongruous, indeed, for us to be discussing the horrors of the Sino-Japanese War and the evacuation of other nationals from Shanghai. Gold and russet leaves rained softly to earth about us and just below, the Severn, in smooth, uninterrupted flow of horizon blue, made its way tranquilly to the bay. A willing captive to serenity, my attention managed to elude the more powerful net of conversation, until someone exclaimed, "Heaven deliver me from such an experience! One week of living in the present Chinese inferno would send me off the deep end, I believe!"

To the speaker's left, the neurologist narrowed eyes. Tamping a cigarette, he commented slowly, "That's not so likely as you think. The average human nervous system reacts more sensibly to extraordinary demands than to an accumulation of minor irritations."

From some memory pit of forgotten things, the Acton girl presented herself suddenly to my attention. Why at this particular moment, I am not sure, for I had no way, certainly, of telling how Miss Acton might have responded to some really great test of the emotions. I glanced up to meet the doctor's quizzical gaze. "Why not share with the rest of us what you're remembering?" he challenged.

"It's not a pleasant tale," I objected, as my eyes once more sought fleetingly the peace of woods and river, "and it would probably be of little interest to others."

A moment of urging followed, then almost before I realized, I heard my voice saying, "Three of us had been on a walking trip through Japan and had ended this vacation in Kobe. It was the summer before the Manchurian affair and those whose loyalties lay with China could still enjoy intimate contacts with Nippon's picturesque land and people. Some friend of Ellen Denning's wished her to ship home a tea set, so Florence Felton and I had gone into one of the smaller porcelain stores with her to make a selection. Unable to please us with anything on the first floor of his establishment, the proprietor had asked with many bows that we ascend a ladder into the loft of the building. There he brought out several lovely samples, and Florence and Ellen had become interested in the relative merits of two designs: one of Fujiyama and one of wistaria vine.

"I left them and crossed the room to a wide casement opening above the street. Resting on the broad sill, I watched Japan's clever copying fingers busy themselves with Western ways. Through Moto-Matchi's commerce trooped school children wearing colorful native kimonos and American fashioned shoes and caps. A gentleman of affairs, garbed in top hat, a Prince Albert suit, and startlingly bright tan shoes, brushed past a woman who clumped by on wooden *geta*, and whose somber outer garments revealed, with each step, delicate rainbow hues. Oriental artistry, I thought, rubbing shoulders with Occidental ugliness, and at what cost!

"Depressed by these sights, I looked across a vista of housetops to a distant hill temple toward which many of Kobe's little thoroughfares seemed to be wandering home. At the foot of the slope the spreading branches of a giant cryptomeria, outlined against the sunset like a design on cut velvet, seemed to beckon a toil-weary people to share in this moment of peace. Almost as one awaking from a dream, I heard Florence protest whimsically, 'But, Ellen, fancy drinking from Fuji daily!'

"Before a suitable retort could be managed, the shopkeeper interrupted the argument by displaying a fresh pattern of blurred green pine branches.

" 'I like that better than either of the others,' I offered, with a glance over my shoulder toward the last, then turned my attention again to the street below. Two people, passengers apparently, from an American liner which had docked that afternoon, stopped to look into the show window directly beneath me. One of the women, large and seemingly genial, was talking volubly; her slender companion replied with an occasional monosyllable only. After a little time, they entered the shop, and, in response to their footsteps, our host directed a nervous eye toward the ladder.

This gesture hastened the choice of the tea set; the pine branch design was selected and we went slowly down the rungs to complete the transaction.

"Artificial light now destroyed the shadowy dusk and presently we were exchanging friendly greetings with the two newcomers. The younger woman was dark, with great, sensitive eyes which lifted an otherwise commonplace face close to the edge of real beauty, but even in repose, she wore an expression of tenseness that interested me sufficiently to ask, 'Have you tired yourself shopping in Kobe?'

" 'No, we came ashore only an hour ago.'

"Here, her more talkative companion, whose name was Simpson, interrupted. 'Miss Acton is on her first trip out to China, and as an old-timer, I'm introducing her to Japan's ports.'

"Beside me Florence was silently studying the girl's face. Ellen, less analytical by nature, smiled and said, 'Like all the rest of us, you'll doubtless find Japan's charm proving a snare to your purse, Miss Acton.'

"The girl looked at her with troubled gaze. 'Charm?' she questioned slowly. 'Most that I've seen so far has been hideous.'

"Like as many parrots, the three of us exclaimed, 'Hideous? Japan?'

" 'Well, I don't know any other word to fit the wretched appearance of the women with black, loosened teeth who helped to coal our ship, or of the little children staggering under sore-eyed babies almost as large as themselves. And certainly there's nothing very picturesque about those hard-driven ricksha men outside—to turn men into beasts of burden seems horrible to me.'

"The speaker's earnestness put an abrupt end to superficial remarks. Florence. usually of few words, was the first to break the silence that followed: 'Every country, Miss Acton, has some distressing conditions, and when you become adjusted to the East, these particular ones will still seem important, but less harrowing than they are now.'

"Color heightened in the girl's face. 'I'm afraid I'll never be able to view such things with equanimity,' she admitted gravely.

"Miss Simpson chuckled, 'She'll get over it!' and after a final, embarrassed sentence or two, we said good-by and left the shop.

"Outside, Florence shook her head in dismay. 'She'll have to learn to weld a personal armor of callousness, and her life equipment seems to contain no tools for that purpose.'

" 'Sounds a bit queer to me,' declared Ellen. 'If this first sight of Japan affects her so, what on earth will she do in China?'

"Rickshas swung toward us out of the dusk, and stepping into them we rode behind swaying firefly lanterns to the group of pines that circled our hotel.

"At one end of the bund in Shanghai," I continued after a moment, "there's a parklike enclosure built on the sea wall that withstands the Pacific's backwash into the muddy Whangpoo. There, until the war put an end to freedom of action, under eucalyptus and ginkgo trees gathered representatives of all the races in the world. On fair mornings, Chinese amahs, chattering and shrilling commands which were seldom heeded, pattered after their undisciplined charges or stopped occasionally to gossip with each other concerning the idiosyncrasies of their respective foreign mistresses. Groups of Japanese business men met to discuss the possibilities of next season's cotton crop in Hupeh, or their increasing textile trade with India. Hindu women, robed and veiled zenana fashion, moved quietly past, and always there might be seen, leaning against the rail and following the ships with restless, homesick eyes, some remittance man or other living in exile on checks that came regularly from solicitors' firms in the Temple, London.

"In the afternoons when Shanghai's offices had emptied and most of the foreign community was busy with tea and tennis, fair Danish or Swedish types shared places under the palms with groups of prosperous French merchants, stout German brokers, Scotch engineers, and Italian sailors, while emaciated White Russians, sober Malays, and an occasional Ottoman in a fez went their lonely ways.

"At this hour about two weeks after the Kobe incident, Florence and I, idling our few remaining days of vacation in Shanghai (Ellen had already gone up the Yangtze to her station, Kiukiang), rose from one of the benches in the shrubbery close to the sea wall and sauntered into the bund. From all directions flowed the ceaseless traffic; motors whose chauffeurs obeyed no laws, natural or otherwise; carriages with drivers lashing furiously at little Mongolian ponies; load-carriers and ricksha-runners avoiding what seemed, even to the practiced eye, unavoidable collisions.

"Florence caught at my arm. Down the street came a group of coolies swinging between them great brown pots of condiment. 'Ali Baba and the Forty Thieves!' she murmured, and we stood enchanted, thankful for the thousandth time that fate had placed us in this land of color and romance.

"Our attention was diverted to a rapidly growing crowd at the Nanking Road intersection. Half curious, we walked in that direction and found to our amazement, the fierce, handsome Sikh in charge of traffic at that point detaining a white woman. Florence gasped, 'Meg, it's that Miss Acton we met in Kobe!'

"Pushing our way through the mob to the two central figures, I asked excitedly, 'What is the matter?'

" 'I struck this policeman,' came the girl's trembling response.

" 'Struck him!' I exclaimed incredulously, 'but why?'

" 'He beat my ricksha coolie and I could not stand it. I think he intends to arrest me.'

"Florence wasted no time on Miss Acton. Instead, she began testing her Soochow dialect on the Sikh, who at first ignored her and then after a moment answered in pidgin English. That he was greatly offended was plain, and as a salve, Florence surreptitiously pressed silver into his hand. This rendered him more talkative: 'He strike me, Mees! Woman, he no can strike me!' The complainant spat on the ground and threatened, 'Next time chop-chop carry Mixed Court!' His eyes still flashed from the indignity as he dispersed the crowd, and Florence thanked him profusely for his patience.

"Within a few moments, we had hurried Miss Acton off to the seat so recently occupied by us in the park. 'I suppose you think I've acted like a child,' she began, struggling to control her voice, 'but I find it very difficult out here to decide about right and wrong.'

" 'What really happened?' I asked curiously.

" 'My ricksha man must have broken some rule of traffic, for the first thing I knew the Sikh was scolding and then clubbing the coolie. I—I'd never seen a defenseless man beaten before and I couldn't sit there and do nothing, so I struck out with my umbrella.' She sighed her bewilderment.

"Understanding prompted me to say, 'I've felt that way myself more than once, Miss Acton. What you didn't realize, though, was that you offered the supreme insult to an Asiatic male: namely, a blow from a woman's hand.'

" 'I'm afraid I didn't stop to think of that or anything else.' As if attempting to explain to herself as well as to us, she added hesitantly, 'I'm more grateful than I can say for your coming along when you did. This is the first time in my life I've ever been involved in a public scene, but out here where there's so much cruelty and injustice, I find myself unable to act calmly.'

"This puzzled humility made the girl seem much more attractive than when in Kobe, and as we saw her safely to her Shanghai quarters, I wondered once again if natures such as hers, which seemed to hold themselves open like raw wounds for the applications of life's salt, were not a decided liability to their possessors.

"In the business of teaching at Nanking I forgot the existence of Miss Acton and her susceptible temperament. The months flew by; Christmas passed and then the Chinese New Year. During this long vacation I decided on two days of shopping in Shanghai. Almost everyone who knew me in port took advantage of this information, so that by the time I set out I had two long lists of purchases to make for others, and the commissions ranged from toothbrushes to a kitchen stove. In an effort to satisfy these demands, I rushed madly around, and in Laou Kai Fook's silk store I was surprised to meet the stout, genial Miss Simpson.

" 'Down for the holidays?' I inquired.

" 'No, I've been transferred to our offices here," she told me, 'and in order to become a stylish Shanghailander, I'm having to buy more clothes. The next time we meet you'll not recognize me.'

"I laughed with her, then inquired, 'What ever became of that Miss Acton you chaperoned on the trip out?'

" 'She went up river to Shasi.'

"I drew in my breath sharply, remembering that Miss Browne who lived in Ichang, had spoken of Shasi as one of the most forsaken spots on earth—with a sinister atmosphere about the place unlike anything to be experienced elsewhere in China. What stupidity of administration had sent this hypersensitive girl to such a place? I asked myself, then added aloud, 'How is she getting along?'

" 'Oh, you know what first-year people are like! Until they become accustomed to things, they have all sorts of curious notions.'

" 'Curious notions!' I repeated inwardly, remembering my own first year and the searing struggle to adapt myself to a strange race and, to what seemed even stranger, members of my own race. It was possible, I thought ruefully, that the first-year people were the only really normal representatives of the foreign communities, but I was careful not to breathe such dangerous doctrine into Miss Simpson's ears.

"Early in July school closed, and Florence and I joined Ellen at Kiukiang for the climb up Kuling Mountain, where we were going to spend the season of heat. We settled down in a small cottage to mornings of language study and afternoons of recreation, until the summer rains broke, putting an end to walks and tennis. Then our spare moments were employed in placing buckets under roof leaks and rubbing mildew from books and clothing. Ellen came out of her room one afternoon holding her new hemp hat from home, its starch all gone and its black surface turned a fuzzy green. Placing it on her head where it drooped in limp folds, she danced an imitative Javanese figure, flapping upturned palms.

" 'Oh, Ellen,' I exclaimed, 'it is ruined!'

" 'No, not really, dear! I plan to startle Shanghai with a new vogue at the end of summer—if I have enough money left to get down there.'

" 'That reminds me,' I said, 'I saw Miss Simpson at New Year's.'

"She and Florence stared at me. 'Who in the world is Miss Simpson?' queried the latter, 'and what has she to do with—'

"'The woman we met in Kobe with the Acton girl,' I explained. 'She's been appointed to Shanghai.'

"Ellen interrupted, 'There, I knew I had something to tell you two! Miss Acton spent New Year's in Kiukiang. It seems her station needed dishes and I suppose they thought the newcomer could be most easily spared; at least, they sent her down to get them. She succeeded in causing a little real excitement while she was there.'

"Florence's interest flared at once. 'What happened?' she inquired, letting both hands fall idly on the sewing in her lap.

"'Oh, she stayed at the Barton house and, of course, Mrs. Barton went with her to shop. Fortunate that she did, too, for I don't know what might have taken place had the girl, with her smattering of the language, been alone! They made directly for Porcelain Street and were soon interested in watching an old artist paint the finishing touches on a nest of bowls. Suddenly, Mrs. Barton was startled by a scream, and turned to see her companion, white as a sheet, pointing to a figure that blocked their way. One of those wretched beggars who practice self-inflicted wounds to compel the onlooker's sympathy had run a sharp, steel knife through his palm; and while the blood dripped slowly downward, he extended the wounded hand in supplication to the girl.

"'Mrs. Barton tossed the horrid creature a coin, took Miss Acton home as fast as she could, administered a sedative, and put her to bed. There she stayed while the hostess tried in every way to rouse her from a settled apathy. One after the other of us ran over there between classes, helped to stuff food in the patient, and talked about everything under the sun that might be of interest. At the end of the week, she was able to board a steamer and Mrs. Barton wired the Shasi Mission to meet the girl in Hankow for the second lap of the journey!'

" 'Then what?' interrupted someone from a corner of the porch.

With an effort I pulled myself forward along Time's crowded thoroughfare to the present. "Ellen had heard nothing further," I told him, "and it was not until two years later that Miss Acton touched our lives again. On Hat-a-men, Peiping, we met Miss Simpson that summer.

" 'How's Shanghai style, these days?' I asked.

" 'Not at all,' came the frowning response, 'I've not seen Shanghai in weeks. What is worse, I am not likely to for more than a day at sailing. They are sending me home ahead of time, with a sick woman whom you may remember —Miss Acton.'

" 'What's the matter with her?' questioned Ellen.

" 'Nobody knows,' Miss Simpson replied wearily. 'That's why the girl's going home—to find out. They have her at the Rockefeller Hospital for observation, but I'll tell you frankly I think she is just plain crazy, and I don't fancy being the guardian on this voyage.'

" 'Is she permitted visitors?' Florence asked.

" 'I can't say for certain, but you might try.'

"The following afternoon, Florence and I walked over to the hospital. We halted at the foot of the marble stairs to enjoy the arching Chinese roof, its colored tiles gleaming in the sun, and a moment later made the abrupt transition to a modern medical world of distinguished specialists and trim American nurses.

" 'Yes, for a few minutes,' a young woman, with a Johns Hopkins class pin on her uniform, agreed to our request.

" 'Baltimore, too?' I asked as we followed down the corridor.

" 'No, Eastern Sho'!' came the smiling reply, and immediately there existed between us that bond, so familiar to travelers from the same state.

"In a willow chair near a window, sat Miss Acton, a shadow of her former self. When we entered, she was staring straight ahead with so set an expression that I felt Miss Simpson was probably correct in thinking the girl mad. Slowly she moved her head in our direction—moved it with palpable effort, as though an invisible force were impelling her in some other pathway of thought—and when she finally recognized us and spoke our names, the normal conventionality of the words startled me. 'This is the first time I've seen you since the rescue in Shanghai, isn't it?' she asked. A faint, chilly smile played flutteringly on her lips. 'How foolish I was those first days; such things do not worry me now.'

"Florence began to talk easily of the delightful trip ahead; a possible stopover at Banff; the latest books to be read on the voyage. The girl's interest quickened to these suggestions for a time, but died before our allotted ten minutes had passed. She seemed suddenly anxious to get back to her own devious thoughts, and we soon left her to them.

"In parting, I asked the nurse bluntly, 'Is she mad?'

" 'Only in her desire to inflict pain, I believe,' she grudgingly admitted.

" 'Inflict pain?' I echoed. 'There must be some mistake—she could never endure seeing things hurt.' Here the nurse's tightly closed lips warned that the discussion was at an end, and after another remark from me about Maryland, Florence and I made our way out. I can still remember feeling glad that Miss Acton was going home where familiar scenes might do their healing work."

"I doubt that they did," commented the neurologist.

For a moment I looked at him. "No, they didn't, for she never reached home. At the end of the month, a cable came to Pei-Tai-Ho, where we were staying, telling of an attempted murder and suicide on board a Pacific liner.

Details followed that a Miss Acton had stabbed her traveling companion with a pair of scissors, had then walked out on deck, jumped into the sea, and had not been found. Her victim, however, was recovering rapidly.

"Tales from Shasi now began to filter through. From the time of her first arrival in that station, Miss Acton had seemed very easily excited and disturbed. It was true that she had met with some unpleasant sights—who did not? She had returned from her visit to Kiukiang nervously unstrung; this had been followed in a few months by a period of serious illness. Then, convalescent, the girl had gone on the street one day and had seen soldiers shoot down a coolie who refused to do their bidding. After that experience she had never been quite the same. The other members of the household had tried to show her something of the pleasant side of life in the East, but they were busy beyond their strength, and all work and no play makes people serious about even trivial things. Miss Acton, studying with a personal teacher that first year, had not the interesting distractions afforded by contacts with children in the day schools or with women in the homes. Things had gone from bad to worse; she had succumbed ever more frequently to these pronounced reactions to suffering. And then, in the third year, her associates began to notice that she was becoming quieter and much more restrained in expression.

"One day, one of the older workers found the younger woman leaning over her desk, apparently amused. She was engaged in torturing a wall lizard, using a nail file to rub off bits of its skin. The spectator, growing suddenly faint, had hurriedly sought her own room. Later the servants began to talk among themselves about the girl's queer actions, and the last straw was added when she plunged a darning needle into the mending-woman's scalp. There was nothing to do but get her away; anti-foreign feeling was strong in Shasi, as it had always been, and to keep someone like Miss Acton in the Mission would be to undo all the labor of years. As it was, she had been sent to the Peiping Hospital and then toward home."

With the narrative ended, the rich silence of the woods was once more unbroken save for the faint impact of falling leaves. After a little while someone asked, "Isn't it likely, Doctor, that the young woman would have ended the same way even if she'd stayed at home?"

"Not so likely, but possible, of course!"

Listening, I thought of those intense, lovely eyes in the Kobe shop and how I had been struck by their beauty; of Florence's analytical interest in the girl's vehemence; of Ellen's remark, "A bit queer!" Well, as the neurologist inferred, no one would ever know, now, whether or not she might have crossed the invisible border line that separates light and shadow in the human mind had she remained in a land where sordid and seamy sights were kept for the most part under cover or, at least, segregated to certain questionable sections of unpleasantness. Instead, Fate had sent her to live where the worst, according to the Westerner's viewpoint, knows no concealment, and where most that is admirable remains carefully hidden from the newcomer's eye. Only when certain of sincere appreciation does the East unlock treasure chests for the stranger. And unaware of the riches which the future might bestow, Miss Acton had been unable to adjust herself to the barren ugliness of her present. Those deep, dark eyes, avid for suffering, had fastened on all that was horrible; and lacking the wholesome strength to tear herself free, their owner had remained to be fascinated, and in the end, destroyed.

THE CLERK

識時務者在乎俊傑

司馬德操

Next to coolies, clerks and apprentices are the omnipresent figures in the Chinese scene. However small a mercantile establishment, it is certain to have at least one apprentice and usually more, who, receiving the three to five years of training according to previously worded contract, will in time achieve the dignity of clerk or accountant.

Boys entering the commercial houses are in a more fortunate group than their contemporaries in the trades; though their status in the social scale is lower, the labors required of them will be less arduous in character than those common to the crafts, and the returns more profitable. Because of these advantages, openings for youthful workers are limited, wherever possible, to family connections, for the successful Chinese is never free from demands of impecunious relatives—a burden of responsibility which he rarely tries to shirk even when it concerns a cousin five or six times removed. This custom serves to contradict the superficial criticism so often on the Westerner's lips—that the Chinese are not charitable. Convinced that "charity begins at home" these money-makers of the nation have little left over for anyone without blood claims.

識時務者在乎俊傑 司馬德操

THE CLERK

Although the mercantile apprentice usually starts out with the special assets of relationship to the owner and an easier type of toil than has his counterpart in industry, the hours of service are just as long and grilling. He is slave to the whim of everyone in the store, and all the tasks no one else desires fall to his lot. For his own mistakes he is punished or beaten, and only too often he is made the scapegoat for those of other workers as well. When this average twelve or thirteen-year-old finally goes to bed, it is to sink into the sleep of utter exhaustion.

Like the rest of his race, however, he learns early to accept endless work and hard knocks as man's common portion; meanwhile he is acquiring what will stand him in good stead throughout life. His master's business soon becomes an open book for him to read, and its pages teach not only all the tricks of trade but how to judge the abilities of customers as well. On errands about town, he accumulates a vast fund of information about his own world of commerce, smelling out items of interest much as a ferret would rats and storing these for future use.

During apprenticeship, the boy receives no remuneration; even when a clerk, his salary may be exceedingly small, but he will put up with this unsatisfactory state of affairs a long time for the sake of security. Having been trained to this business, his determination is to remain in it, and every energy will be exerted to make himself indispensable to the management.

To this end there will be added to the accumulation of information gained during apprenticeship, knowledge of dialects not native to his locality and smatterings of whichever foreign languages may be most useful to his work. Expert though he may be with the abacus and the Chinese system of accounting, he will miss no chance to learn typing and other commercial skills introduced by foreigners. None of these extra activities are permitted to interfere in any way with duty to his employer, and usually their acquisition comes only as the result of ambition and a capacity for industry beyond the experience of the average American or European.

In Shanghai, for example, over a period of years, night-school courses have been offered by various mission organizations and the Young Men's Christian Association. These classes have been crowded by young men ranging in age from sixteen to thirty, in search of such subjects as English and bookkeeping. After a working day from six in the morning to seven at night for many, they sit in these student groups several hours, three or four evenings each week, then go home to prepare for the next class before retiring.

識時務者在乎俊傑
司馬德操

識時務者在乎俊傑 司馬德操

As additional labor, those in the bookkeeping groups, unable to afford the expensive paper required for the double-entry system, have even been known to buy the cheaper plain sheets and to rule lines and columns in red and blue ink on these.

Deh Hsiao in *Friendship Circle—Chinese Design* is a common example of hundreds of young men like him in China's commercial life.

霍林路

FRIENDSHIP CIRCLE—CHINESE DESIGN

When he permitted memory to recall the affair, which was seldom, Deh Hsiao told himself that it seemed a peculiarly ironical twist of Fortune's Wheel for the trouble to have occurred on his first anniversary as typist with the Central China International Trading Company. He could still remember the glow of achievement with which he had entered the office that morning, and the ensuing surprise as he realized that the date meant nothing to anyone but himself.

Himself and, to be exact, the comprador! That worthy, who managed all details of employment for the firm, had told the young typist early in the forenoon that the latter's salary would be increased in the future by one dollar each moon. This, after a year of service, was the custom, as was also the comprador's habit of bestowing such favors on the basis of twenty per cent commission to himself. For the first of these Deh Hsiao was grateful—for the second, he knew little resentment. Eighty cents was eighty cents, and that he held this position at all was, even after a year, so remarkable a circumstance that not yet had he become accustomed to it.

The interests of the Central China International Trading Company were woven like multiple strands into the pattern of the city's life. Through the window nearest him, the typist could pick out, one after the other, junks that floated the flag of the organization. On shore, above the tide-reach, the largest of all the godowns to be seen wore the same emblem, and between its gateways, as well as through those of several storage places at strategic points about the city, sweating, half-clad load-coolies filed in endless parade. With these evidences of financial power, all of the local and provincial world was familiar; what was less commonly known was that the Central China International Trading Company began and ended with one personality alone—the fat, astute merchant, Chen Kuen.

In the early days of his employment, Deh Hsiao had returned each night to his home with Chang, the money-changer, and there, after the evening meal, he had related the interesting incidents of his occupation. "The greatest men of this city pass the desk where I sit outside Chen Kuen's own private room," he would tell the elderly Chang importantly.

Chang's old eyes would narrow in a smile as he quoted, "There was once a crow who in the company of golden pheasants thought himself their brother." Then to remove the sting from this, he would continue, "Your merchant, Chen Kuen, is shrewd beyond most men; also, he has Fortune's own gift for friends."

Deh Hsiao would gulp down Chang Housewife's steaming food and think to himself that the speaker also knew something about friendship. Otherwise, where would he, Deh Hsiao, be at this moment?

Four years earlier the youth had been one of a horde of starving flood refugees who had swarmed into the city overnight. With home and people gone, he had, after several days of food searching, sunk exhausted on the curb before Chang's money shop, and a little later had found himself on a stool just over the threshold, with a bowl of rice gruel clutched between his hands. That had been the beginning, and due to some sudden impulse on the part of the childless proprietor, there the boy had remained.

In the dusky front room with its iron-grated counter Deh Hsiao had learned to make himself useful at the business that went on inside its four walls. His fingers grew deft in slipping over the wires of the abacus, and, as he listened to the numerous customers seeking an exchange of currency, his quick ears began to pick up fragments of their cosmopolitan speech—Russian, Japanese, English, and a half-dozen native dialects as well.

"Words," Chang had told him one day, "stick to you as does glue to rice paper."

Ambition stirred suddenly in the youth's mind, and shortly afterwards he begged permission to enroll in an English class at a free night school. Later he had set about mastering a typewriter, and through this accomplishment had come his connection with the Trading Company.

His first thought had been to refuse the offered position, even though it seemed the chance of a lifetime. "Why?" the money-changer had wanted to know, "is this not the reason you studied—to earn money?"

"And shall I repay your great kindness by leaving when I can be of use? Here in this shop is my place—here I remain!"

"I am not yet so old that I cannot care for this business," Chang had replied with unusual gruffness. "These others will pay you good silver and of that you may share with me."

Somewhat confused about how he might best serve his benefactors, the youth had finally gone to Chen Kuen's, and for a year of twelve-hour days, had worked at typing or accounting or listing incoming and outgoing cargoes. He was unfailingly interested in the bustle and excitement that went on about him; and shortly after the conversation with the comprador on that eventful first anniversary, an unusual commotion caused him to look up from his work toward the outer office.

In the doorway stood four soldiers in official livery, bodyguard for a tall, thin, young man before whom the manager bowed ceremoniously. The guest was ushered into the private sanctum of Chen Kuen himself, where tea and sweetmeats were ordered served at once. When these trays of refreshment were brought, the typist noticed that they held the best the establishment could offer.

Within a few minutes the servant reappeared empty-handed. Deh Hsiao glanced up in surprise—an interview which spent so little time in social courtesies must be out of the ordinary, indeed. Pondering this, he lifted a sheet of paper to the machine and as he did so, a faint clicking informed him that the door to the owner's office had come ajar. The employee's first impulse was to reach over and close it, but curiosity concerning the sounds floating out to him delayed action.

Merchant and guest were conversing, not in the customary Mandarin speech, but in a dialect peculiar to a province on the coast. The listener strove to recognize the phrases. There was something about looting soldiers and the terms, "General Ling," "friendship," "His Excellency," were repeated again and again. *Ai*, if only that down-river speech were more familiar! Little sense could he make out of this jumble, and with his desk full of work, there was no time to waste in further guessing. As he stretched out an arm, the expression, "Fanmakers' Way," caught his attention. Instantly Deh Hsiao was alert.

"Why that road?" demanded Chen Kuen, reverting suddenly to the local Mandarin tongue.

"Nearest the end of the city where they camp!"

"The foreign section would yield greater spoils."

"Of a certainty! But the foreigners suspected such a move; two gunboats steam here from Kiukiang. Ling is not prepared to draw their fire. You understand the situation?"

"If his forces are so weak, why then does the city government fear? Have we no troops of our own?"

"Not enough! And had we twice as many as the War Lord, are His Excellency, the Mayor, and Ling to destroy by combat a friendship of thirty years?" The visitor's tones were smoothly polite. "Unnecessary is it for me to remind you, Most Honorable Merchant, that His Excellency does not treat these affairs lightly. Otherwise, would he have troubled to warn you about saving the goods in that godown?"

Deh Hsiao smothered a gasp. Never had he heard anyone address the head of the Central China International Trading Company in this fashion. A grave silence followed, and in a pretense at industry for the benefit of clerks close by, the typist caught up a brush pen and began checking an account. When the voices resumed, they were again using the coastal dialect, and a little later the guest was once more escorted across the room and attended courteously on his way.

Following this departure the comprador was closeted for an hour with Chen Kuen. This time the door was tightly closed and Deh Hsiao heard nothing of what went on inside. He cared little. Already his head was whirling. Ling, the War Lord, who held half of the province in his hands, who had forced the civil governor, Liu, to flee for refuge, was in camp close to the city. But, because of old friendship for the present chief official, Ling was permitting this rich prize among Yangtze ports to remain almost unmolested. One demand only he made—that a section be allotted his ill-paid soldiers for looting. This condition which might ordinarily have been of minor importance had placed the Mayor in an awkward position, for within the district specified stood a godown that belonged to another and almost equally powerful friend, the merchant, Chen Kuen. Co-incidentally, His Excellency had accepted the terms of the first and had warned the second. That his consideration was benefiting other particular individuals also he might have been surprised to learn. This time the emissary was to be an insignificant typist, and the object of friendly concern, the proprietor of a small money shop on Fan-makers' Way.

How he endured the remainder of the afternoon, Deh Hsiao could not have said. As yet he had no idea when the soldiers would enter the city, whether this night or another. At the close of business he would hurry home to Chang's, help the elderly couple to be in readiness for flight, and then await the firm's preparations concerning that particular godown. Dusk was already shading the offices when his desk was cleared. He rose, carried the papers to a senior clerk, and prepared to leave. As he did so, a call came for him from the comprador's office.

"Work there is still to be done," began the manager, "and the others to whom this might be trusted are busy elsewhere. Get food on the street, then call a ricksha and ride to our warehouse on Fanmakers' Way. There you will find the watchman and load-bearers awaiting. The first shipment, which goes on a Shasi junk tonight, is one hundred large tins of tea and fifty bales of raw silk. The seal on each box of tea will tell the quality of the contents; list these carefully. When all of the loads are ready, you will accompany the coolies here."

"Here?"

"Here! I shall need your reports for the Customs Officer."

"And afterwards?"

"You will return to the godown for further work."

Deh Hsiao moved slowly away. To protest orders would be to incur the manager's anger and perhaps lose this position. Obeying as swiftly as possible, he would then hurry to warn Chang. That the looters were coming tonight was now certain; they were, however, not likely to appear before their intended victims had retired and the streets were free of pedestrians. Indignation kindled within him—not one thought had the Chief Official or Chen Kuen given, apparently, to these helpless, law-abiding citizens who were to be sacrificed to military greed and cruelty. Liu, the deposed governor, had been a good man. During the four years of his rule, the province had known little fighting. If only Liu might come again into power and defeat Ling for all time!

When he reached the godown, he was surprised by his first glimpse into the storage space. To one side box after box of valuable ginseng met his eye; to the other, rolls bearing the stamps of Chefoo pongee and Nanking velvet were piled high. At the rear from floor to ceiling he could see bales, but there was no sign of tea. He took out the record book, and as the watchman ordered the coolies to pull forward the bales, began to make out a statement.

As the last bale was dragged outside, he noticed in the dim light that the tea had been stored behind this barrier. Deh Hsiao turned to a bearer, "Now those boxes over there," he ordered, "and let me see each seal as you pass them along!"

The man reached for two, then grabbed wildly as one overbalanced and fell to the floor.

"A veritable water cow in a porcelain shop! Look, you have broken the seal of that one!" exclaimed the clerk with a glance at the tin. Repairing the label, he thought irritably, would steal another minute or two from his precious time. "Set it over here," he added, and examined the second one.

"Not my fault!" sullenly protested the coolie. "You said it was tea—am I to be blamed that it was not?"

"Tea it is, of a certainty! Another, and this time be careful!"

Muttering to himself about weights, the man obeyed. His companions now joined in the work and the remaining tins went forth. When the last had been checked, Deh Hsiao leaned over and lifted the damaged container. That coolie had not been at fault, he told himself—no dried leaves weighed this much. Cautiously he looked toward the noisy group beyond, then, prying the lid where the seal was broken, stuck his fingers within. Tea met first touch, but from beneath this top covering he pulled up a narrow box of cartridges.

Amazement seized him. The unchanging policy of the Central China International Trading Company was to handle no munitions. Small wonder that these containers, so carefully labled for quality, had been hidden behind bales of raw silk! *Ai-ya!* who could say what might be in those fifty bales themselves? Of all the valuable goods in this godown, these were to be removed first—shipped on a junk to Shasi. Startled, he repeated the name to himself. Shasi was where Liu, the former governor, was supposed to have fled. How stupid, in all of today's happenings, not to have recalled once that Liu was still another of Chen Kuen's close friends.

For a minute grim humor made him forget worry about Chang. Ling, the War Lord, having mercy on the city; the

Chief Official warning Chen Kuen about stored cargo; Chen Kuen hastily salvaging Liu's ammunition, which Liu at the very first opportunity would use on Ling! And all for friendship! How the gods must be laughing at this chain of man's making!

Footsteps approached. Deh Hsiao concealed the cartridge box, closed the tin deftly, and stepping forward, asked the watchman for rice glue to mend the seal. A half hour later he had placed the lists in the comprador's hands. The manager scanned them with a hurried eye, then announced gruffly, "This time one of the other clerks goes with you. Hurry a little—there is yet much to do!"

As their two barefooted ricksha-runners slipped along the rapidly quieting streets, Deh Hsiao made his decision. He had no idea how long this new task would require and he must reach Chang without further delay. "Pull-cartman," he called softly, "listen as you run!"

The slap-slap of the coolie's feet did not falter, but his ears strained toward the passenger.

"Pick up a stone between your toes and you shall gain in fare, I promise."

A hundred yards farther on the runner slid to a halt, lowered the shafts, and grumbling realistically, began to examine his foot. The vehicle with the other clerk swung past, then prepared to stop. "Do not wait!" Deh Hsiao shouted, "time must not be wasted. I follow."

When they had passed out of sight, he continued sharply to his coolie, "Turn back to the next street and take me to the farther end of Fanmakers' Way!"

On arrival he discovered with relief that Chang had not yet boarded the shop for the night. After paying and dismissing the coolie, he hurried across the threshold.

"You are late," commented the money-changer.

Without a word Deh Hsiao led the older man to the living quarters at the rear and told him the story. An hour of feverish activity passed before the couple's personal valuables had been collected and most of the shop's currency counted and stowed in a small chest. These were placed in a ricksha, and with Chang Housewife as passenger to guard them, were dispatched across the city to the home of relatives where the old lady would spend the night. Her husband decided to remain in his store. "Soldiers wreak the worst fury on abandoned property," he reminded; "I will offer no resistance and they will take these coins left on the trays and go. Have I not lived through many such affairs?"

Still protesting at this arrangement Chang Housewife finally rode off. "Now," urged Chang, "call another ricksha and hasten to your work. I will not soon forget the risk you have faced."

"And what of you here alone?"

"I go to whisper in the ear of a friend or so, then I board up this shop and retire. Lay down your heart!" Chang comforted. "If Ling and the official have an understanding, there is nothing to fear but petty theft."

An hour or two later Deh Hsiao again returned to Chang's door. He had arrived at the godown too late to be of much use, and soon afterwards when soldiers appeared, he had joined the watchman and others in flight. Resistance by unarmed citizens to troops was a useless gesture, as the law-abiding had learned from long centuries of bitter experience.

What really mattered to the young man was the sure knowledge that, had he been at the warehouse earlier to help, more could have been saved, and for this he would undoubtedly pay. Watchman, clerk, coolies—all could testify to his delay. "*Muh iu fa tz!*" he sighed. Even though his position might be gone, no alternative course had offered itself. For his benefactor's sake he must, in case of dismissal, make a pretense of continued employment and later think of a good excuse for being dropped. Chang must never know how much this affair had cost the one he had befriended. "You are safe?" he inquired as the money-changer admitted him.

"Safe, although one twisted my arm, thinking I had more silver hidden about this house. Finally they satisfied themselves with the coins left for that purpose." He sighed ruefully, "They took also the bedding, and when the mistress of this house learns that—*ai-ya!*"

Deh Hsiao was forced to smile at the other's woebegone expression. He was not smiling, however, the next morning when he found on his desk a summons from the comprador. For a heavy moment he stood holding the slip of paper in his hand. About the offices groups of employees shared newspapers and discussed the events of the preceding night in excited tones. Soldiers, supposedly Ling's, had looted one end of the city, including the firm's own godown on Fanmakers' Way. Good fortune it was that two late shipments had left the warehouse only a little before the looting occurred!

The typist listened without attention. There was nothing he could do but face the manager and accept dismissal. But was that true? Shared secrets were, on occasions, advantageous weapons. In his possession at present was information which he was certain Chen Kuen would not wish known and, were he to threaten disclosure, it was possible that the comprador would make terms.

A sense of loyalty within the youth protested. Through the comprador, Chen Kuen had given him, an inexperienced typist, a position for which there had been numerous applicants. They had paid him a fair wage, and only yesterday that wage had been increased. Even with this weapon which a cunning Fortune had placed ready to his hand, he knew himself defeated. Besides his own obligation to the firm, there was also ingrained in him a racial respect for the quality of friendship which had made Chen Kuen risk his own great reputation last night. Even as he realized these things, a newer hope stirred in his mind. Perhaps, if he told the truth, the manager might understand. *Ai!* He sucked in his breath—to tell the truth would be to reveal that he had listened to a conversation not meant for his ears. *Muh iu fa tz!* That was of all things the last, for to lose face by such a confession would be even worse than being discharged.

When he entered the comprador's office, the latter looked up coldly. "So, you have come! Last night, due to your neglect, this establishment lost goods of value. There is no further work for you here," he finished with an air of finality. Then, as though memory had suddenly prodded him, the older man added, "Before you go, one question I wish to ask. In that shipment for Shasi, a box of tea bore a broken seal. Was that your fault also or someone else's?"

Deh Hsiao's heart missed a beat, but he managed to answer steadily, "The coolie who passed the tin to me dropped it."

"Tell me his number that he may be taught care."

"He was not to blame, Honorable Sir—the box was heavier than the man expected. When I examined it for damage, I discovered that for myself."

There was a long silence. Finally the manager broke it. "Last night in your report, you did not mention this."

Deh Hsiao gestured in explanation: "Whether the tea was heavy or light was not my affair."

Under the comprador's steady gaze, the discharged typist found the moment one of strain. There was to be, doubtless, no further discussion. Turning to leave, he heard the other's voice say, "To know when to speak and when to remain silent is a virtue possessed by few. Those bills for the Ichang office go on the night steamer; when you have prepared them, help the senior clerk on last month's accounts!"

Sudden relief made the young man feel faint. Bowing, he returned to his desk, fed a billhead into the machine, and began to write.

THE BEGGAR

The whole of Nature is the property of
even the poorest man.

天不生無祿之人
古諺

Perhaps the most unpleasant of first and ineradicable impressions made upon the foreigner in the Orient is that of hordes of tatterdemalions, maimed, halt, and blind that spring up like mushrooms wherever his feet touch the soil. At sight of them horror and pity supersede all other emotions in the stranger's breast, and he is apt to throw away substance feverishly in the effort to be rid of their presence. It soon becomes apparent, however, that this method achieves the very opposite of the effect desired, for the glint of copper or silver instantly increases the number of suppliants sevenfold, and the impulse to benevolence dies a natural death.

As experience broadens, the newcomer learns that among these mendicants, whose name is legion, only a minority are direct victims of adversity. In this latter class are temporary refugees from the sudden disasters of war, flood, or famine; the afflicted from families too poor to support a pair of idle hands; or community outcasts such as lepers.

Exclusive of these, however, beggary for the great mass is a profession chosen in preference to a life of labor by creatures who are well aware of their value as community nuisances. In contrast to all other careers,

天不生無祿之人古諺

this one demands that its representatives capitalize defects; mutilation of the body is a requisite, and the lengths to which they will go to make themselves sufficiently abhorrent in appearance to the spectator are beyond description. One of the commonest practices is that of placing a small child in a pottery jar, permitting only its head the freedom of growth, and in due course of years setting this pathetic monstrosity free to make its appeal. Matted hair, wounds, sores, filth, and rags are all a part of stock in trade as are also fawning and whining.

From the beggars' standpoint, the returns for selling their birthrights of self-respect and decency are satisfactory. Chained by no routine of labor, they come and go where and when they please, and in the end receive a much more generous mess of pottage than ever falls to the lot of the hard-working coolie. His ramshackle shelter and threadbare garments are little better than theirs; his food is nothing like so certain or so plentiful; and his body wears out long before its time from strain and exposure such as they are seldom called upon to endure.

It is difficult to say when these parasites first became organized into guilds. Beggars are referred to in the ancient *Book of Rites* and, at a fairly early date in history, Chinese officials attempted to limit their activities by appointing over each group a headman chosen from their own number. This appointee automatically became responsible to the District Magistrate for the behavior of all in his profession. His chief duties were to discipline the troublesome and to sign a contract with each merchant of the community who in return for an annual monetary assessment was promised exemption from annoyance by all members of the organization thereabouts.

A red-paper agreement to this effect was posted conspicuously on the wall of every establishment concerned, and individual mendicants having attention called to the familiar document usually went their ways without further ado. Occasionally some recalcitrant soul would refuse to acknowledge authority in such form, though in this event the merchant had the privilege of forcible ejection. Were the misdemeanor repeated, the Beggar King, himself, took a hand at punishment, and death to the rebel was a not uncommon result.

This traditional arrangement between beggars and shopkeepers still persists generally, for most merchants find attempts at evasion much more costly than the tax itself. The presence of these undesirables will soon drive customers away, and the price that the business man pays for independence is to have members of the guild descend in hordes on his establishment. When

天不生無祿之人
古諺

天不生無祿之人古諺

this happens, the proprietor has no other recourse than to put up with these villainous ragamuffins, knowing that if he attempt to use force in expelling them, they will at once wreck building and stock.

With private citizens it is an unwritten law that on festive occasions such as births or weddings, beggars shall be given their share of the feast itself, or a gift in silver, and most householders, recognizing the ease with which these pests can ruin such affairs, abide by the custom. Besides the general means of income, guild members have, as personal funds, donations from benevolent passers-by, though on this largess there is no monopoly, and wandering beggars from other sections offer unceasing competition.

As might be expected from such an existence, this class represents the lowest dregs of humanity with all society as its natural prey and, when thwarted, its members are often actively dangerous. However, even among outcasts there is to be found occasionally one in whom persists the racial traits of humor and appreciation of beauty. Of such was *Clever Eel.* Removed early from the environment in which evil inheritance had placed him, it is possible that in time he might have become a worth-while citizen like some of those remarkable examples of beggary cited in China's historical lore.

霍林路

CLEVER EEL, PHILOSOPHER

In the last of those sagging huts which, with ten or fifteen more, constituted one of Wuhu City's begging communities, Clever Eel woke himself with a prolonged snore, then rolled tightly in his filthy *pu-gai* for another nap. A more vicious nip than usual from a flea decided against this plan and the fourteen-year-old now threw the cover from him and sat up to scratch. Trying, through layers of ragged garments, to capture the offender brought no results, and, as Common Sense had warned him in advance, the activity merely stirred up a host of these guests which were being entertained so unwillingly by his body. Sunlight was already shining through the cracks of mud wall, and since further sleep at present was impossible, he jumped to his feet and stretched.

A centipede hunting for vermin in a trash pile under the table suddenly caught the youth's attention, and seizing a small iron bar he went after the hideous crawler with determined purpose. This adversary, although darting about with incredible swiftness, was at least to be fought in the open, and when the bar came down at last on the long, toughly skinned creature with its ugly, orange head and numerous legs, Clever Eel grunted his satisfaction. The scuffle roused the rest of the family and his mother, cursing sleepily, demanded a reason for this unwonted disturbance.

"I killed a centipede!"

"Good that your father was not here to wake!" came gruffly.

Clever Eel made no comment on this obvious truth. Taught from babyhood that centipedes, scorpions, and lizards were enemies for man to avoid, he knew, nevertheless, that had specimens of all three been present when his father was trying to sleep, they would have been permitted to go their dangerous way at will. Fortunately the head of this house conducted his affairs usually while others slept, and his arrival at home was always the signal for his offspring to leave. The eldest son wondered ever more frequently what pursuit might engage a beggar's attention at night, but he knew better than to put the question.

Hunger now urged him to action and, accustomed to living by his wits, he disappeared through the doorway and set out for the mud flats in search of possible provender cast up by the river overnight. In a quavering falsetto, he began to hum two or three bars from a tune which a wandering fiddler had played on the Wuhu City streets the night before. Up and down went the song, becoming with each repetition more of a screeching outlet for his exuberant spirits.

He stopped to squeeze soft mud between the toes of one foot and, as had been anticipated, felt something wriggle. The humming ceased while his hands dug industriously. After a moment or two a piece of rotted bamboo lying close by was brought into use, and with this, he succeeded in stirring up a hard, slippery body. For a second his fingers closed over it, but the agile sand crab slid to freedom and, squirming more deeply underground, left an angry trail of bubbles in its wake. Disgusted, the hunter jammed the end of bamboo down the hole and went on his way.

A sudden odor of freshly baked *hsao-ping* reached his sharp nostrils. This hot, brown pastry would make an excellent breakfast, and in a moment he had traced the scent. Just ahead, on a small, level space beside stone steps that climbed from the water to the city streets, Old Fu had put up a square of matting roof on four bamboo poles and was busily laying out foodstuffs on the wooden table beneath. When this was done, the vendor would settle down to sell his tempting stock at prices which would vary with each customer's ability to bargain.

Clever Eel, trying to decide on a course of action that would supply him with *hsao-ping* at no cost, stood and eyed the stall from a distance. He and Old Fu were not friends, but intimates—much too intimate, Old Fu would have said if asked his opinion of the young beggar who pestered him daily. In their affrays the more agile youth usually came off victor, but he had a few poignant memories of the strength in the old man's arms on certain past occasions, and these had taught him to walk warily. Also, the food vendor, who refused stubbornly to pay the fee to the Beggars' Guild which insured most merchants against annoyance by members of that amazing organization, had threatened once or twice to call police, and at the thought of this possibility, the boy's skin prickled. A trip to the *Ya-men* was not to be lightly regarded, but much worse than that was the certainty of punishment at his father's hands should the Law's attention be drawn to their roof.

Falling back a few steps, the boy now climbed a slope about forty feet above the food stand. Fu, still unaware of the other's proximity this crisp wintry morning, sat on his small stool with hands folded in opposite sleeves for warmth and watched a weather-beaten junk unfurl sails to the breeze. A swift slap of the wind and the ship's canvas swung around, knocking overboard one of her crew.

The food vendor and Clever Eel, from his point of vantage midway to the summit of the hill, rose at the same moment to see who would win out in this contest between the River Dragon and a man. Then recognizing in this circumstance an amazing opportunity to further his original purpose, the boy slid down the slope like a cat and, before the merchant could withdraw attention from the river drama, the young thief, a *hsao-ping* clutched in each dirty paw, had scrambled again up the hill. There looking back for his pursuer, he chuckled and sat down to enjoy the booty at leisure. Approaching Old Fu's place of business was Seventeen, one year older than himself and sworn enemy, but as long as this second representative of the beggar community remained close to the food stand, the vendor would not dare to leave his supplies. Clever Eel smacked lips over the last crumbs, belched loudly twice, and turned his attention again riverward, in time to see the terrified sailor scramble over the side unaided. No one on board had lifted a finger in the rescue—no one dared; wise men did not thwart the Dragon in search of prey. The youth shivered, and then, because drowning was a danger which faced him daily, immediately forgot the incident.

He looked up and down the swift flowing Yangtze. Small craft everywhere were crowding the water. There was a chill in the air, and those who had two sets of garments were already wearing them. In his own case cold mattered little; beneath his tatters was a warm padding which would not be removed until the next spring's heat should demand such a change. Clever Eel rarely experienced the discomfort and hunger known to sons of hard-working coolies; what was even more unusual was that, except for a few minor scars, he had been called upon to endure none of the deformities and mutilations which were a part of almost every beggar's physical equipment. His mother had tricks of her own for kindling sympathy. A rubbing of red ink paste into a healed wound had an excellent effect on kind-hearted passers-by, and when such simple ruses failed, the agonizing contortions of limb in which her family had been trained achieved almost certain results. The woman in his house had a full head on her, he thought proudly; when she considered the painful methods to which her neighbors resorted, she expressed herself with shocking frankness concerning people who had no brains for otherwise misleading the spectator's eye.

To the west a wavering line of warm, gray smoke now penciled itself against the fresh blue of the sky; one of the large river steamers, an important source of livelihood for beggars, was on its way from Hankow to Shanghai. Clever Eel set off on a run for home and, reaching the doorway, first assured himself of his father's absence, then called out, "Fireboat comes!"

His mother and three younger children were engaged in sorting heaps of old rags and papers, previously collected on the Wuhu streets. This loot had many uses; some of it might even be sold, and until that happened, storage in the one-roomed hut cost nothing but the trouble of stepping over the trash.

Like a jewel in a dustbin there appeared against this background of filth and disorder a spray of golden shrub which Clever Eel, running after a foreign woman's ricksha the day before, had begged for his own. The delicate bloom now stood spending sweetness in a broken vase from a city junk pile, and the boy narrowed eyelids in admiration, while he waited for some response to his announcement. He stooped over and picking one of the small golden blossoms from the brown stem stuck it in a nostril where it would remain for an indefinite period. By this means even away at work, he could enjoy the perfume to the full.

His mother now rose, drew her rags about her, gave orders to the other children, and, catching up the baby, led the way out. The son followed, carrying in one hand a long, bamboo pole; with the other he dragged by a rope a large, round, wooden tub, flat-bottomed, about four feet in diameter and twenty inches in depth. Two small paddles lay in the bottom, one for use and one for emergency; with this equipment the trio was prepared to meet the Yangtze's angry current.

Down across the mud pattered these scarecrows; the steamer was already docking and about its sides swarmed sampans. In them sat representatives from the Wuhu shops carefully holding cotton bundles in which their samples of stock were tied. Later these would be offered to the admiring attention of steamer passengers and sold, unless the travelers should be old-timers, at several times the real value.

By the river's edge, mother and son launched their tub, then backing water until the steamer had made fast, they remained as close to the larger vessel as the current permitted. Clever Eel now searched for holes in the small cotton bag on the end of his pole while the mother prepared for business by surreptitiously pinching her baby, an unfailing stimulus to a series of lusty yells. In this way even the youngest member of the family contributed personal services toward accumulating income.

Today the child's cries attracted the attention of two passengers leaning on the deck rail. Looking down, these saw a poverty-stricken mother of sadly drawn countenance holding a screaming child in one arm, and with the other paddling strenuously to keep a tub in position against the steamer hull. Beside her in this bobbing craft a third tatterdemalion stood with amazing steadiness, lifting to the steamer rail a small empty sack which told its own story.

Trained from infancy in detecting the first stir of sympathy, Clever Eel now swung the bag close to the hands of the two staring travelers. Distorted of feature, he went through his regular plaint of no father, no home, no food, no clothing, and besought these fortunate foreigners to spare a destitute widow and orphans but the tiniest morsel of their plenty. His immediate audience, tourists who had been visiting in Hankow, understood nothing of all this jargon, but such appearance of distress was more than they could endure and, reaching in his pocket, the man flung a silver Mexican dollar into the sack.

The size of this donation was so overwhelming that for a second, the recipient stared open-mouthed at the coin which he had drawn back to him with lightninglike speed. *Ai-ya!* Here was silver enough to buy a month's food for a man. That all foreigners were queer everyone knew, but this one must be empty-headed, indeed, to part so easily from wealth. A sudden prod from his mother's foot returned him to normalcy, and bowing elaborate thanks to the philanthropist, he resumed his whine for the benefit of newcomers on the deck. Some of these watched the tub's approach with interest; one or two contributed small coins; but no one repeated the startling munificence of the first gift.

Gradually the paddlers rounded the stern. There a tall figure leaned over the rail and smiled dryly. Up went the pole and sack, together with the customary wail. This passenger chuckled; fragments of excellent Chinese floated back to the tub: "*Tiao pi-sha bah shi-dsang deh hun-ni puh iao chien—ni pih o hai pan.*" ("You worthless, filthy street urchin—you do not need money—you are fatter than I.")

The genial tone in which these uncomplimentary remarks were couched appealed to a sense of humor in the occupants of the tub; Clever Eel and his mother both grinned. Here was no arrival of yesternight; this foreigner was not to be fooled, and, with impudently assumed gravity, the young beggar bowed low in the tub. He then swung the pole back into its former position and spoke with all the dignity of an official: "Honorable Hsien-Seng, it is as you say—thin I am not, but I have ten mouths to fill with rice, and nothing is left for the gods. For that reason only do I beg.

If your generosity permits a small offering for the shrine nearest our home, my family will be grateful to the tenth generation!"

The foreigner, unable to control mirth at this sudden change of front, laughed heartily, then tossed a copper into the sack. "For thy incense and rice!" he replied in solemnity, "and may such devotion be duly rewarded!"

One of the ship's officers walked along the deck in their direction. "*Chu-bah!*" he barked down to the tub, the words so wrapped in a Scotch burr as to be unrecognizable, but there was no mistaking the sound of authority behind them. As the occupants moved on in response, Clever Eel winked companionably at the recent donor, and called back the usual parting phrase, "*Tsai-hwei!*"

Soon afterwards, with their morning business completed, the beggars paddled back to shore. The contents of the bag now reposed safely within the mother's rags. "Today our fortune is great!" she remarked aloud, then cautiously tightened her lips in self-reproach. Even if no human were close enough to hear such boasting, one never knew what evil spirit might be eavesdropping. Halfway to the hut, she left her son in charge of baby and wooden vessel, and walked to a street of food shops.

When enough for a feast had been purchased, she returned to find her youngest offspring playing contentedly in the tub, while Clever Eel and Seventeen engaged in battle.

These combatants, occupied in trying to tear the rags from each other's body, interspersed their labors with verbal vilification of character and ancestry. A crowd of interested onlookers gathered around and into their midst strode the mother of Seventeen. "What is that filthy worm spawned by snakes doing to my son?" she demanded loudly.

Clever Eel's parent laid her bundles in the tub and moved forward to make suitable reply. "Your son—a decayed, maggot-filled egg if there ever was one—spends his days keeping good citizens from work and——"

"Good citizens! Work!" interrupted the other woman screaming with laughter and glancing from one spectator to the other for appreciation, "*ai!* that one whose husband's head will some day be nailed to the city gate, talks of good citizens, while that creature she bore in a mud puddle, kills my poor, fatherless boy."

Well simulated astonishment spread over her opponent's face. "That I have lived to this day is beyond belief! Yet you yourself have said that the young turtle there is fatherless although nine men have lived under your roof, or is it ten? Poor am I at figures," she told the crowd apologetically, "and today worse than usual. Hearing truth from a liar spends the listener's strength as well as the speaker's."

Seventeen's mother, fully conscious of the widespread amusement at her expense, was by now purple with rage.

For a moment the swift rush of words choked her, then becoming more coherent, she went on venomously, "For seven generations that one's ancestors have been two-hundred-cash women in the town where I was born, and it is said that one of them even mated with a monkey. True or not, I cannot say, but certain it is every woman of her house chatters without ceasing."

Unfortunately, this speech failed to reach the ears for which it was intended. Clever Eel's mother had seized her own last line on which to depart, and now having administered stout kicks to each of the boys involved, she caught up the baby and proceeded toward her hut with the calm indifference of royalty toward the mutterings of slaves.

Her son, dragging the tub and its contents slowly after him, knew a slight discontent. Early in the tussle his fingers had discovered a box of foreign matches hidden in Seventeen's garments. Had the women continued their argument a moment longer, those always useful fire sticks would now have belonged to him. Also, though vaguely, he felt let down by the recent quarrel. His mother's insults, for instance, had lacked their usually strong quality; he, himself, could have thought up many more forceful ones. He sighed.

Later at home, sitting beside a bowl now emptied of good food, the youth cracked watermelon seeds between his teeth and breathed renewed satisfaction. His eyes fell on the branch of golden bloom and lighted with pleasure. Somewhere in the excitement he had lost the flower from his nostril, but here there was no need for such borrowed sweetness.

Once, roaming about Wuhu, he had poked his head within the window of a private school, and, resting arms on the sill, had watched boys who had nothing to do but study. There was a deafening noise about the classroom; each student was repeating his *National Reader* aloud, but above the din rose the voice of the old, gray-haired teacher reciting wisdom from the sages. Clever Eel recalled a proverb about its being better for a man to be poor and feel rich than to be rich and feel poor. At the time the statement had seemed very foolish. Well, he had been very young then; it must have been almost a year ago, and only today had understanding come. His stomach was amply filled, eyes were happily satisfied, and his mother would doubtless show more ability in the next neighborhood fracas. He felt like an early Ming emperor. His eyelids closed in heaviness and, rolling over on a *pu-gai*, the youth fell asleep.

雞羽檄示速疾也見漢高祖紀

THE POSTMAN

Chi mou pao—If in haste, dispatch a chicken feather!

You must know that by the great Khan's orders there has been established between those posthouses, at every interval of three miles, a little fort with some forty houses round about it, in which dwell the people who act as the emperor's foot runners. Every one of those runners wears a great, wide belt, set all over with bells, so that as they run the three miles from post to post, their bells are heard jingling a long way off. And thus on reaching the post the runner finds another man similarly equipped and all ready to take his place, who instantly takes over whatsoever he has in charge and with it receives a slip of paper from the clerk, who is always at hand for the purpose; and so the new man sets off and runs his three miles.

Moreover, there are also at those stations other men . . . who are employed for expresses when there is a call for great haste in sending dispatches to any governor of a province, or to give news when any baron has revolted, or in other such emergencies. . . . These men travel by horse with regular changes of steed . . . and the speed at which they go is marvelous. They could never do it, did they not bind hard the stomach, chest, and head with strong bands. And each of them carries with him a gerfalcon tablet, in sign that he is bound on an urgent express; so that if perchance his horse break down, or he meet with other mishap, whomsoever he may fall in with on the road, he is empowered to make him dismount and give up his horse. Nobody dares refuse in such a case.

—*Travels of Marco Polo*

When Messer Marco Polo, in the thirteenth century, wrote this description of the Chinese Post, the system was already ancient in age. The "Foot Service," known as *Yu*, is mentioned in accounts of the Chou Dynasty (1122–255 B.C.) and fully detailed references to it occur in the annals of the Han Era (202 B.C. to A.D. 220). During this later period, the "Horse Service," or *Chi*, of which Polo speaks, was also established a thousand years or more before the young Venetian was astonished by its smooth efficiency.

If the message to be transmitted were official in character, the runner, or rider, carried a *Hsi*, a small wooden tablet one foot two inches in length, according to Yen Shu-ku, and to this was attached the symbolic feather which Messer Polo romantically and perhaps truly terms "gerfalcon," but which Chinese sources tell us came prosaically enough from the wing of a farmyard chicken.

Whatever the symbol they bore, certain it is that these early carriers of the post possessed qualities of courage and endurance which seem to have been passed on down through the ages to their successors, for China's

雞羽檄 示速疾也見漢高祖紀

雞羽檄 示速疾也見漢高祖紀

modern post-runner, except in sections where western machinery facilitates transportation on land and water, faces dangers that differ in small degree from those of two thousand years ago. The Upper Yangtze Gorges offer just as many rapids and whirlpools for the small post boats to negotiate as they did during the Han Dynasty; and floods, plagues, and bandits continue to present their terrors to the lonely traveler on China's roads.

Today the Chinese postman is shorn of glamour. Carrying neither official tablet nor the symbolic feather to attract attention, he cannot, even for a moment, pose as a national hero spreading the news of foreign invasion or of internecine strife. Telegraph and radio have already cast on the gerfalcon's flight an air of absurd futility from the dim past. And, if in pacing his familiar route, the modern runner sometimes pauses to gaze enviously as an airplane freighted with momentous communications drones overhead, he does not stop for long. Work is his to do and the time for accomplishment limited. In pleasant, but businesslike fashion, he goes faithfully about this more humdrum routine, carrying his share of those perishable rice paper missives of joy or sorrow, enmity or friendship, wealth or poverty to four hundred million souls.

霍林路
中華郵政

CHEN, THE THIRD, DELIVERS THE MAIL

Chen, the Third, wedged in the mass of human creatures crowding the cabin wall seat, shifted crossed legs for momentary freedom of muscle, wiped the sweat from his face and head, and cast a somber, indifferent glance at the other passengers. In the past six months as district postman he had become used to this overloaded Foochow launch, but today the stream of men, women, and children boarding it had seemed endless. There was no longer an inch of unoccupied space in the cabin, and that the deck was as completely packed was proved by the absence of light and air which filtered usually through the narrow windows into this room.

The opening at Chen's back was blocked by an opium smoker, whose emaciated shoulders fitted neatly into the narrow slit, his vice published to all about him by the cloying odor of the drug. On the bench opposite, a fat official, garbed in the finest quality of pongee, shared candy and watermelon seeds with his wife and three sons. A countrywoman fed a solemn-faced baby a long, green cucumber; a slender, scholarly figure huddled over a volume of poetry, and three merchants passed a water pipe among them, each taking one gurgling puff from its brass container. One of them yawned; a second stared at the old teacher's book, then engaged him in conversation concerning the relative merits of Li Po's and Tu Fu's poems.

Chen, the Third, strained to listen to this but the whining voices of children fretful from the heat drowned the more subdued tones of literary discussion. The official's wife watched her latest watermelon seed shoot across the cabin and laughed aloud. The young postman eyed her with distaste. She might be wife to an official and the fortunate mother of three sons, but one who cared so little about attracting attention knew nothing of polite custom. He wondered idly if all of these cabin passengers were fleeing from the cholera scare in Foochow to less congested areas. Certainly the scholar was not; he who lost himself in classic wisdom spent little thought on the body. The official would run probably at the first whisper of danger; on the other hand these merchants had, doubtless, important business in Kucheng or Yenping, and would return promptly to Foochow.

No one could ever tell into whose bosom cholera would next strike terror! The "spitting blood" disease was queer, indeed. His land knew other plagues as devastating, but none had the power of this one to poison men's minds as well as bodies. Perhaps it was because the Cholera Demon conceded no off seasons. Each summer with the arrival of Great Heat its search for prey began. Like the python in sacred Ku-shan's temple it rose regularly from periods of dormancy to demand food. The priests were hard pressed at such moments, to satisfy the serpent's hunger, but the Cholera Demon, Chen, the Third, thought grimly, needed no intermediary service. When desire touched this scourge, quarry was not difficult to find. His skin crawled; he had seen victims of the disease in their death struggles, and the memory was not a pleasant one.

Even this fearful subject could not hold his thoughts long from his own special misery of mind. At twenty-four, when one's future lay in ruins before his feet, all other calamities seemed of small importance. Six months ago, due to good rating in the city service and to the friendship of the old postman who had previously held this route, Chen had received the river appointment. With today's journey it would be annulled, and he told himself bitterly for the hundredth time, through no fault of his. The newly arrived inspector from the Central Government had made that fact clear. There had even been a word of commendation to soften the announcement that they wished a man of riper age in so responsible a position. Each month this particular district, harassed by bandits, by political agitators, by looting, unpaid armies, became a greater hazard to the post, and the authorities felt it wise to have a representative on whose shoulders years weighed more heavily.

Chen, the Third, had listened respectfully and said nothing. Why waste words on one whose ears were already sealed to argument? He had accepted the decision, collected the mail for his district, and seen it safely on the launch. As yet no one had been told of his ill-fortune. There would be plenty of time for such news to spread when he again reached home. And who, he asked himself, would believe that no slightest blame attached to him in the matter? No one, except Mei-dih, his wife, and perhaps the old postman who knew much of government officials and their whims.

He rose, picked his way with difficulty through the throng, and climbed to the deck. Pushing through the jostling mob, he secured a footing by the rail and watched the treacherous rapids and whirlpools of the Min swirl beneath him. Men who had named this river "the Snake" had chosen aptly. And what the inspector had said about other dangers was true enough. Bandits and disorganized troops were a constant menace. He supposed he was not overly courageous, for the thought of facing either chilled him to the bone. Well, in the future he need worry about none of these; there were, after all, some advantages in being demoted to his previous local route in Foochow, as Mei-dih would be careful to point out in an effort to lessen his disappointment. A good wife she was, gentle and soft of speech and, to her honor, the mother of his three-year-old son!

While his mind clung to these comforting relationships, the port began to assume shape in the foreground. Sampans, slipper boats, and junks rubbed one another for choice anchorage; boatmen mingled snarls and laughter; popping firecrackers announced the departure of a loaded cargo, and coolies fought for a fair distribution of loads. As soon as they had made fast, Chen saw to the immediate transference of second- and third-class matter to the smaller boat on which it would travel up river, then turned to Li, one of the two postal runners for the overland journey, who had just arrived.

"Where is Sia?"

"I have not seen him," Li replied as he stooped to the sacks of first-class mail.

"Perhaps he is waiting at the post office," suggested Chen equably. When one remembered how far Li and Sia would have to run in today's heat, allowance might be made for a few moments' delay at the start.

At the post office there was still no sign of Sia. Instead a message from Sia's village, a short distance away, explained with cold finality that Sia would not only do no running under the present scorching sky, but that his feet would never again press these roads with which they had been familiar for years, for Sia lay in his father's house dead of cholera.

Li's face whitened. "Only yesterday he was here!" he said shakily.

Chen made no reply. All his interest was centered on the one to fill Sia's place. In his six months' service, he had never before been confronted with the problem of finding a substitute runner. "Who," he demanded suddenly, "carries the post when you are absent?"

Li, still dazed, replied haltingly, "No one; I am always here."

"But is there no other registered in this town with the postal service?"

"No one but Sia—" Li gulped nervously—"and myself. There was Wang, whose appointment I received. He stopped because of bandits."

"Does he still dwell in this town?" With eagerness Chen grasped at the possibility.

"No. Moreover, do you think one terrified of bandits would not fear to run in a dead man's shoes?"

"Then who is to carry Sia's share of the mail?"

Li shrugged his shoulders free of responsibility. "If the post boat has not already gone, perhaps the crew will take that along with the other."

His companion discarded this idea promptly. "And ask some of the people in this district to wait a week for important letters? No!"

"Have you a better plan than that—good!" Li lifted his allotment. "The day grows older," he added warningly.

Chen felt the web of responsibility tighten about him. One thing hammered at his brain: the post must go through as usual, and with Sia dead and no other carrier registered, there remained only one person to run the first lap with Li, and that was himself. If the gods chose to heap this final bit of ill-fortune on top of his dismissal, there was no help for it.

He turned sharply to Li. "I go with you in Sia's place." Then writing a hasty note to the Foochow postmaster, he gave a coolie the message and a coin, and directed him to the captain of the launch.

Li watched him amazed. "But you cannot run so fast as I," he protested.

"Then you will have to walk more slowly!"

Later Chen smiled wryly to himself. What Li had said was true indeed. This effort to keep pace with the other's dogtrot taxed him to the utmost. There was not even the relief of talking; a man's entire strength went into speed. He felt himself slipping back through the centuries to those days of ancient runners who wore the symbolic feather on their garments and delivered the emperor's mail on time or paid with a life.

For the first village there were few letters. Chen eyed a teahouse with longing, but Li did not halt. They pressed on steadily under a merciless sun. With relief he saw another group of huts come into view.

Here there was mail for the innkeeper, and the runners took advantage of the stop to order bowls of tea. Famished, Chen gulped at his drink. Li, who seemed unwearied, talked with the proprietor between sips. The room was dark and cool and, save for themselves, empty of customers. Chen, relaxing gratefully, heard the innkeeper ask, "Is that a new postman for this section?" And Li's reply, "No; in Sia's place."

"Where is Sia?"

Li answered with hesitation, "Dead!"

"*Ai-ya!* And of cholera, is it not so? From every village come the rumors of death. Here two men and a woman are no longer with us. Who can say where it will strike next?" His voice lowered.

Li glanced fearfully over his shoulder, as though expecting plague to pounce on him from the shadows, then resumed the journey at once. Hastening after him, Chen wondered why one with courage to face the constant dangers of the road should be so fearful of this particular evil. Sia and Li had, however, been intimate companions, and it was possible Li felt that the disease in seizing his friend had missed his own body by the narrowest of margins.

The afternoon wore on; a series of small settlements alternated with hot, dusty stretches of road. At sunset they saw the mud walls of the little town where Ling would relieve them of the remaining mail for the second lap. The environs seemed strangely deserted; none of the usual vendors offered their wares about the gateway, and a number of vultures perched ominously upon a stretch of wall. Afterward Chen realized that had he been less weary he would have reckoned these signs at their true value. As it was, he moved on mechanically until a sudden yell from Li brought him to a standstill. "What is the matter?" he asked, startled.

Li, his eyes fixed in horror on the ground, swayed like a bamboo in the wind. A choking stench assailed the nostrils. Chen sniffed curiously, and then he saw. Lying just beyond in the gateway was what remained of a human body, and tearing savagely at the flesh, three mangy dogs fought for possession.

Chen was the first to recover himself. With difficulty he withdrew his gaze from this macabre spectacle as Li seemed about to retreat. "Come!" he ordered, pushing the other through the gate with him, "let us find Ling!"

His own thoughts were chaotic. This last had been almost too much to bear and Li looked ready to die. There was something very peculiar about the appearance of this whole place; shops were either boarded up or their fronts yawned darkly empty. Two tattered beggars were all that remained of the normal bustle and excitement on a main street. A muffled wailing rose from somewhere, and stench increased sickeningly. Li's feet lagged, but Chen urged him forward. "Where is the post office?" he asked.

Li, preoccupied with terror, managed to mutter, "The first turn of the street."

When they reached the spot, the narrow, rectangular sign for "local bureau" swung before a small, closed building. A hollow echo was the only answer to knocking, and Ling was nowhere to be seen. On the next doorsill, an old crone huddled. Chen called to her, "Grandmother, where is the manager of this post office?"

She lifted rheumy eyes to his face, but said nothing. He repeated the question to no avail. Up the street a girl of eleven or twelve years strove to comfort a whining infant. Near her sprawled a sleek, overfed dog with twitching, distended belly. From time to time its sleepy gaze lifted to the children and at these moments the girl flung small bits of stick and refuse at it. At his wits' end, Chen moved forward. "Little Sister," he asked, "are your parents within?"

The maid's painful concentration on the animal drifted to this stranger. She nodded a vague, "Yes."

"May I speak to them?"

Wonder spread over her face. "They are dead."

Her questioner stepped back a pace. *Ai-ya!* what next? His knees were trembling. "And is there no other in your house?" he continued.

"I and this man child." Her voice changed to a plaintive note. "Sir, there is no food and we hunger. And the dog—the dog would go within." She began to whimper. "I am afraid."

In despair the young man listened. Was he caught in some awful nightmare, or had he died and passed to the nethermost Taoist hell?

Li's voice sounded, prodding the old woman with questions. He turned sullenly to Chen. "She says the post office has been closed all day. For days many deaths have occurred here—that I already knew—and last night few families remained untouched. The elders offered much money to the priests, and hours were spent trying to exorcise the Cholera Demon. But by dawn still more were stricken, and the priests said the town was accursed. All who were able fled." He flung his sack down on the flagstones. "And I do likewise! My work ends here. I wait no longer like a fool to draw this evil on my head——"

Before he could complete his sentence, the old woman screeched shrilly and clawed at her abdomen. Li needed no further impetus; he began to run madly in the direction from which they had come. Chen, panic-filled, followed closely, his mail sack flapping heavily with each step. It was not until they had left the town a quarter mile behind that he stopped for breath and watched his companion hurry from sight. There was not now any need to keep up with Li, the way back was clear. He sank down by the roadside, removed cap and jacket with trembling hands, and stretched out, head resting on the bag. After the day's unusual strain, his body seized eagerly at this chance to rest, and as his breathing became less labored, his mind drowsed.

Some disturbing finger of his brain pricked him to consciousness. He sat up and looked about him. Dusk was touching the land with gentle shadows. Well, he had better go on, he thought wearily, and put an end to this futile journey. He would carry this mail back to the town where overland service began and then—! Good! What then? Catch the next launch to Foochow and return to headquarters? Walk in with this pouch of letters and say, "Here is today's delivery for my district, but not all; the rest lies in the street of a deserted town"? Watch the under clerks gasp, then strive to conceal their amusement; listen while the inspector remarked, "You understand why we must have an older man to meet emergencies?" Later see disappointment creep into the old postman's eyes! How could he ever face the old postman who had believed him equal to the demands of this position? As for Mei-dih's faith in his ability to meet any situation—what of that? But already he had gone far beyond all that was required technically of him; that Sia had died and Ling failed to appear was not his fault. Did they expect him, he demanded in self-justification, to cover Ling's territory also? Li had felt *his* responsibility end with the usual run. As Li had said, a man was a fool to court disaster openly.

From the depths of his mind an old proverb emerged: "He who knows what is right and does it not—he is a coward." Chen squirmed uncomfortably. "Who can say what is right?" he inquired of the open fields. "Night falls and I know nothing of that road."

"A coward! A coward! And your son shall copy your ways!" jeered the grasses, swaying in a sudden gusty breeze.

Viciously the young man rose, put on the discarded garments, and reached for the sack. Once more he would try to find in that caldron of terror some living creature who could point out the road. With a nervous contraction of his throat, he turned again toward the town.

Picking his way carefully through the darkened gateway, he hurried on with occasional furtive glances about him. Each shadowy door was a yawning pit from which evil might emerge to grasp him. His body was clammy with cold and his teeth chattered. A child suddenly cried out. The little maid! He had forgotten her entirely, and in the face of her desperate plight his own danger seemed to lessen. "Small Sister," he called, "it is the postman again."

The childish form holding the baby was wedged in the doorway, still attempting to act as barrier to the dog which now pawed snarling on the sill. Chen felt courage return to him as he gave the beast a swift shove and sent it howling up the street. "Now," he continued, "listen carefully, Small One! Do you know which road the postman travels?"

"That way," she pointed in the darkness.

"Then come with me!" he ordered, stooping first to grope about for Li's sack which lay unharmed where it had fallen in the street. He added its contents to his own bag while the little girl shifted the baby brother to her back and obediently led the way through the blackness. When the fresh air of the farmland blew about them, the sound of voices reached their ears—a woman's high tones among them. The two wayfarers halted. These were not bandits, certainly! Chen listened intently, then called out. Questioning revealed them as refugees from the town, and in a few moments he had left the children in their care, borrowed a lantern, and obtained further directions.

At the next village all was quiet, but he beat on the gate until an excited householder wished to know why hard-working farmers should be aroused from their beds at this hour. Progress was necessarily slow for names as well as communities were unfamiliar. At one settlement dogs attacked him, but he beat them off until help came from their owners. Dense thickets of bamboo alternated with low, winding foothills. Once an ugly, venomous head reared itself threateningly in the path, only to glide sinuously into the grass. His foot struck a soft, slippery mound and he fell headlong. A wild boar rose from beneath him, snorted angrily, then disappeared. The lantern, strangely enough, was still burning. He held it high as he ran on.

Two more stops were between him and the river, where his task would end. As dawn lightened the sky, he caught the first sparkle of swift-flowing water. At the bank a small boat carried him across to the city

"Who are you and where do you come from?" was the postmaster's surprised greeting. "Last night I telegraphed about the mail, but as yet no answer has arrived." He eyed Chen's disheveled appearance with a dry grin. "What happened—did bandits capture you?"

"Bandits only I did not meet," retorted the postman wearily.

With the mail safely delivered, he was at last free of burden. At Foochow he would hand in his report with a clear mind, then settle down to his former position. Later, on the small boat rushing down-river, he slept.

When he finally reached the Foochow office, an account of his journey had already preceded him. "Today's delivery has gone by boat all the way," his chief told him. "It will continue to do that until dependable men can be appointed to take the overland route. Go home, rest, and prepare yourself for regular service the day after tomorrow!"

"That will be where?"

"Where but on the launch as usual?"

Chen, the Third's, head swam. Was he dreaming again? "But the inspector—" he protested.

"The inspector! *Ai*—that fellow! He has gone back to his own place." The postmaster caught up a pile of reports, checked one, then spoke again, "Moreover, did the inspector not say that we needed especially men who would know how to meet emergencies?"

The younger man's spirits soared. So he was to have his own district, in spite of the inspector! As for dangers to be faced in that appointment, what did they amount to? His work was once more safe in his grasp!

With twinkling eyes the postmaster peered at him over horn spectacles. "Of course, if you prefer local service—it can be arranged!"

Chen looked up startled, then, responding to this banter with a grin, expressed his deep appreciation and left the building. In the street he looked neither to right nor left; as though his body had never known weariness, he rushed home to Mei-dih and his son.

THE CHILD

The great man never loses the heart of a child

大人者不失其赤子之心者也
孟子

When a son is born to Chinese parents, Classic Learning counsels that he be wrapped in royal raiment and given a scepter for plaything. In direct contrast, a daughter must be content with swaddling of coarse cloth and a broken tile for entertainment. Receiving congratulations over the birth of a boy, father and mother respond, "Great happiness is ours!" For a girl they acknowledge, "Only small happiness!"

These items, small in themselves, are nevertheless straws which indicate how China's wind of opinion about the sexes has blown for many hundreds of years. Resembling similar viewpoints in other Oriental countries, it is probable, however, that the Chinese attitude has, from the first, been motivated not by determination to subjugate women but from practical reasons. Viewed realistically, a daughter in an old Chinese family was an economic liability and nothing else. She meant the extra expense of food, clothing, shelter, and dowry to her household, and in return for these she could neither add to income nor serve before the ancestral tablets, as did her brothers. Throughout the formative years she must be trained thoroughly in all domestic affairs, be taught proficiency in every type of

大人者不失其赤子之心者也 孟子

handiwork, and disciplined into a paragon of virtue and propriety that she might not shame her parents in the marriage they had worked hard to arrange for her. When this ceremony occurred, usually at the age when she was becoming most useful in the home, she lost, once and for all time, her own family identity in that of her husband's. To the average maid and her blood relations, death could have made scarcely more severe or more lasting a separation than did marriage.

That daughters were generally undesired, however, is not true. In the homes of the middle class and the wealthy, a girl was as likely to be the household pet as elsewhere in the world. Sons were of first importance, but even in families lacking sons, there were numerous instances of cherished daughters. When these showed aptitude for learning, as many did, they frequently received an education equaling that of their brothers and with the additional honor of having their fathers as personal teachers.

In the peasant home the problem was vastly different. There a daughter's arrival added to the depths of trouble in which parents and overcrowded family were already involved. She represented to those around her another rice bowl to be filled from a supply so meager that those now sharing it were always on the verge of starvation. If she lived, it would be to

大人者不失其赤子之心者也 孟子

decrease daily the present slender margin of safety these others possessed. Accordingly the new girl-child in this impoverished household often knew birth and death in the same moment, and her mother, weeping over that scrap of flesh and blood for which she had travailed in vain, knew the sad comfort that this infant, at least, would not live to become a "potbelly" strung to skin and bones, like her living sons and daughters.

In such families every child, boy and girl alike, was assigned regular tasks from the time he could crawl. Frequently forced to bear burdens too great for them and to labor far beyond strength, they led, nevertheless, a more normal life than that to which foreign factories and mills introduced them in port cities. Even girls became economically valuable in these hives of industry, and for years empty streets at dawn have echoed familiarly the weary footfalls of these children on their way to, or returning from, a twelve-hour shift. A thousand ills have been the possession of these young hostages to man's greed, and the National Government was working to improve conditions when Japan's guns put an end to many of the establishments concerned and to most of the helpless children who filled them.

For the more fortunate Chinese child the first six years of life are joyful and carefree. A mother, or

大人者不失其赤子之心者也 孟子

wet nurse, suckles the baby until it is three years old. During this period and often longer, the youngest under the roof rules with a hand of iron. When the simplest desire is thwarted, a fit of temper ensues and the most outrageous naughtiness brings only gentle reproof. In fairer emotional weather the child is irresistible. Garbed in gaily-colored duplicates of its parent's clothing, and these are as expensive as the family exchequer permits, the youngster meets the world with a mixture of courtesy, mischief, and preternatural gravity. Plump, satin-skinned bodies, keen, black eyes, rosebud mouths, and dimpled cheeks are the common possession of both sexes.

Through these years of early childhood, boys and girls play together at a game resembling hopscotch; test skill at kite flying, top spinning, or tossing a shuttlecock; learn nursery rimes and folk tales, and delight in peep shows and trained mice performances.

At the age of six, however, the dividing line is sharply drawn between the sexes. The boy is placed in a school or under a private tutor's guidance; the little maid's freedom is limited more and more to the women's apartments. There, she receives the necessary instruction in routine household affairs and learns her lessons on conduct from the classic *Four Books for Girls*.

THE CHILD

With amazing swiftness these children, now living in adult worlds, assume responsibility, developing that poise and graciousness so typical of their race and seeming to prove the Chinese theory that "the mischievous child makes the useful man." What is more likely to achieve this rapid maturity is that with babyhood over, the boy and girl soon learn that age, not youth, holds the position of importance in the household—a theory in direct contrast to that of the West in such matters.

Big Sister Lin in *War Is for Men, Not Butterflies* is representative of the children in China's great farming class. Persecuted by flood, famine, and civil strife for years, they have known little but suffering, and today, each exploding shell from Nipponese guns adds more of these pathetic victims to the ever-increasing list of China's slaughtered innocents.

大人者不失其赤子之心者也

孟子

大人者不失其赤子之心者也

孟子

霍林路

WAR IS FOR MEN, NOT BUTTERFLIES

* * * *International Press Bulletin:* At noon today the foreign invaders are within one mile of the city's South Gate. All villages on the way have been burned and the inhabitants killed. By midnight, it is reported, the city will be in the enemy's hands.

Big Sister Lin, cramped between Mother and six other passengers on the wheelbarrow, swung her cold feet to the rhythm of the squeaking vehicle, watched the golden lights of night flare into being, and thought that she had never known such happiness. After all these weary moons of worry and hardship, they would once more have their home in the fields beyond the city, and Father—she repeated the word over and over again—Father would be there to care for them.

Until three years ago when Big Sister was Peach Blossom's present age of nine, they had known no life save that of the little farm. Food there had been and decent blue garments; warmth when the weather was bitter; and in summer heat, the willow pond for coolness. All day long Father and Mother had worked with the soil while Big Sister cared for Peach Blossom and the two baby brothers. And then soldiers had come—soldiers who urged farmers to seize their landlord's property and keep it for their own.

"Fool talk!" Father had dared to say and the angry soldiers had pressed a gun between his shoulders and marched him off as prisoner.

Other hard-working farmers had fared the same, and their families had been driven off the land that furnished their livelihood. With no safe haven in the familiar countryside, these refugees had drifted eventually to the port city, there to seek food and shelter. Police of many nations patrolled this metropolitan area and protected its inhabitants from straggling groups of armed men who taught strange doctrines. Thanks to Kuan-yin, Mother and Big Sister Lin had found work in a silk filature, and settled in a rented room above a grain merchant's shop. Peach Blossom had remained there to care for her two small brothers.

It was not a very good room. Little light seeped in through the slit of a window, and holes there were through which the rats that throve on the grain supply below were sometimes chased by the landlord's cat. But these things were to be expected. If only the walls could be made to keep out wind and rain, there would be no reason for dissatisfaction. Many worse rooms there were, Big Sister knew with a wisdom far beyond her twelve years, and their recent good news, alone, had put an end to Mother's plan of seeking out one with a lower rent than was now paid.

Yesterday afternoon Mother had gone on the street to buy food for evening rice, and there before the shop entrance, she had met a neighbor from their own farmlands. In a moment he had told her everything: Father had been released after more than two years with his captors and was again working his plot of ground. Grief, however, had changed him into an old man.

"And why not?" demanded the neighbor. "Does not Lin Farmer think his wife and children long since dead? Good Fortune surely must have brought about this auspicious meeting!" he continued, for having finished the errands in the city, he would stop at Lin Farmer's door on the way home and tell him where to seek those from whom he had been separated for so long.

Mother had returned with the good news, weeping as Big Sister had never seen her weep since the day Father had been marched away. All night long at the mill, tears had continued to course down her cheeks, as she spun the silk threads on reels. The forewoman had scolded, but what cared Mother now about harsh words? Before the sun had risen thrice, they would be already on their way back to the farm.

Big Sister readjusted to her wrist the round, bamboo basket which held a midnight lunch of boiled rice and condiment, and snuggled her free hand with its scarred, washerwoman fingers under Mother's arm. Her parent smiled down at her. "What is it?" she asked.

The little girl shook her head. "Nothing—I was just thinking a thought." Then after a minute she said, half to herself, "Too hard to believe is it that Peach Blossom will not have to work in the mill."

Her mother nodded assurance, "No, Small Sister will not work at the vats, and the boys will grow up to be farmers like their ancestors."

Mother was thinking of the little brothers, but Big Sister's mind was on Peach Blossom who was unlike anyone else in the world, at least in Big Sister's, world. Peach Blossom's eyes, set like miniature, glowing lanterns in a delicate, moon-shaped face, had the power to make Big Sister, and sometimes even Mother, forget the twelve hours of toiling at the mill. And when her smile failed, Peach Blossom used other charms. Lilting phrases about stars and trees and butterflies slipped from her soft, red lips as easily as most children said "Yes" and "No" and "What is it?" Daily she kept the little boys enthralled by her tales of what the grain merchant's cat and the thievish rats found to say to each other. But her most fascinating character on these flights of fancy was a yellow butterfly—an enigma, indeed, to the little brothers, who were acquainted with one only by hearsay.

Butterflies there were in the city—in the parks and gardens, but not in the dingy street where the grain merchant dwelt. The boys had long forgotten creatures of the countryside, and Mother sometimes wondered why Peach Blossom had remembered a butterfly better than other natural delights—this Small Sister who constantly forgot so many more important things: who let the coals die to ashes and good rice scorch, when only the tiniest spark of memory was needed to save them at the proper moment.

Mother did not understand Peach Blossom, but Big Sister did. The younger girl had no interest in housework. Her mind was clever and her small, slender hands did beautiful things with a needle. Big Sister thought of her own hands and what the mill had done to them. Days of stirring silk cocoons in vats of boiling water, that their strands might soften and yet not tangle, soon cooked fingertips. One had a short stick, of course, but so often that missed its depth and the fingers entered instead. There were times, too, when eyelids refused to stay open and the treasured cocoons were left for the moment to go where they pleased. But only for a moment! Big Sister shuddered as she recalled the punishment that always followed. Each of her hands held dark, red scars where the forewoman had plunged them to the wrist in the scalding liquid. Once a sleepy child had fallen head first into the vat. Whenever Big Sister recalled this accident, she saw her own small and forgetful sister in the dead child's place. Peach Blossom, she told herself over and over, must never, never work in the mill.

But there was now no need for this to happen, and Big Sister smiled to herself in relief. Suddenly the wheelbarrow creaked to a stop, and with Mother and the others, she alighted and climbed the path to the filature. As they entered, the sound of shots came from a distance. For days there had been tension about the city; the workers spoke of battle and troops, but Big Sister knew no fear. Here in this great place one was not unprotected as were farmers. Moreover, the thought of Father's coming filled her mind to the exclusion of all else. She moved in the file of children toward the vats as Mother took a seat beside the winding reels. A few more days at most—perhaps tomorrow—they would leave this place forever!

*** *International Press Bulletin:* Two hours before midnight, the enemy forced entrance into the city. For a time, there was fierce hand-to-hand fighting, but the poorly equipped defenders were outnumbered three to one. Bodies of dead and wounded Chinese, unarmed civilians and soldiers alike, crowd the streets. As yet no casualties have been reported in the Foreign Concessions, though Americans and Europeans are tense with anxiety over a threatened air raid.

During the night a deafening explosion shook the filature building. Glass broke in several windows and a breeze from the river swirled in. Machinery was stilled instantly and the workers rushed to stuff up the holes. Even on the hottest of summer days, the rooms in the mill were kept closed that no breath of air might twist and break one of the thousands of delicate silk threads in the process of being wound. When the last draft had been checked, questions surged into speech. "What was it?" "Did shots hit the mill?" "Shots would not make so great a noise; perhaps, an earthquake——"

Those in authority frowned on the temporary idleness, and in another minute, the resuming whir of machines drowned out the voices. Periodically the same deafening noise was repeated, but no more glass was broken and work proceeded as usual. Women, not daring to take their eyes from the task in hand, strained necks in attitudes of nervous listening. Big Sister Lin wondered gravely if all were well at the grain shop. She wanted to glance toward Mother, but she dared not remove attention from the vat. Not until the whistle blew for the morning shift did she breathe with relief.

In the long line of men, women, and children to whom labor had granted another brief respite, she passed into the yard and a gray, misty dawn. Surprisingly, that early morning quiet, with which she was so familiar, today did not exist. One detonation followed another; the sky was a dull red in color; and strangest of all—a mere handful of workers waited to enter the mill. Big Sister stood by Mother and listened while the new arrivals spoke of a night of horrors. The great noise was due neither to earthquake rumblings, nor to shots, though of these last there were plenty. Bombs were the cause, falling from airplanes—bombs that exploded on the roofs of houses or in the middle of thoroughfares, destroying all with which they came in contact. Nowhere was one safe. Simply in coming to work they had risked life, and at this very moment, the homes they had left might be burning.

Aghast, the horde of weary laborers milled about the yard, undecided what next to do. Mother's hand tightened on Big Sister's shoulder. These two, at least, had an immediate purpose: they must reach the children. Neither their own wheelbarrow, nor any other on which to ride home, was available. A ricksha, expensive as it might be, would have to be used. Big Sister cupped hands to mouth and shrilled, "*Hwang pah chae!*" But no yellow, rubber-tired cart appeared. Despairingly Mother looked down at her bound, crippled feet, then clutching Big Sister, started on the mile and a half walk homeward.

In this section streets were deserted. After a while their ears grew used to the bombing, and with the approach of daylight, hope rose that the neighborhood about the grain shop might be safe. As they neared their own district, other sounds clamored for attention. Mother halted before taking a next tortured step, and listened with increasing terror. The sharp explosion of bullets mingled with the screams of people. What could be happening just beyond a separating street or two? In this present state of affairs they would not wait for Father to come for them; today she and her children would start out for the farmland. Enough there was among her hoarded coins to pay third-class fares on the train, and as soon as she reached the room over the grain shop, packing should begin. She began to hobble more swiftly.

*** *International Press Bulletin:* Before daylight airplanes zoomed over the Chinese sections of the city dropping bombs. Already entire streets of civilian residences have been destroyed and foreigners are now preparing for immediate evacuation from the Concessions.

As Mother and Big Sister turned a corner, the mob met them. Individuals, groups of two and three, ran madly past. Their faces were contorted with terror. Soot and plaster and blood stains smeared their garments. Mothers and children swayed under the weight of babies; men shared the double burden of old people unable to walk, and of household treasures. All moved forward as in a nightmare, looking neither to right nor left. Mother and Big Sister Lin, pressing against a house wall to escape being trampled underfoot, found strength to call out, "What is happening?"

No one answered. Clinging to the walls, their desperate figures pushed on toward the grain shop. Only a little farther and they would be in their own street. Unexpectedly the crowd increased and the two were wrenched sharply apart. Mother was carried with the tide in the opposite direction, and Big Sister, marooned safely for the moment on a doorsill, screamed, "Mother! Mother! Mother!" and then succumbed to panic.

No one glanced at the shrieking huddle in the doorway. After a while, exhaustion did its kindly work; and the little girl's sudden hysteria changed from broken sobs to a mood of active responsibility. She rose and stepped forward. To her was left the task of reaching the children at once. She could be sure that Mother would join them as soon as was possible.

For a time the crowds lessened and, weaving through them and the billows of smoke, the child reached home. Few people appeared on this street, and there was no fire. Trembling, she climbed the steps to the upper room and entered.

Pressed against the narrow window slit were Peach Blossom and the two little brothers. The boys were watching their small sister's face with grave interest as she pointed to the sky and told them of the most recent exploits of her friend, the yellow butterfly.

Big Sister, unexpectedly nauseated and weak, sank on a stool. The children were safe, and she might now lay down her heart. When Mother came, they would all have morning rice and then go to sleep.

From where she sat, there could be seen, above the three dark heads, a small, window-framed picture of the sky. Clouds rubbed out the morning sunlight, and a great bird winged its way across the shadowy background. Big Sister shivered. An airplane! What was it the men had said about airplanes? Bombs! What were bombs? In growing fear she called out sharply, "Come here!"

Startled, the three children turned in her direction. "When did you come, and where is Mother?" they wanted to know.

Peach Blossom moved closer and studied her sister intently. Her eyes widened. "Did you catch some of the butterfly's firecrackers?" she inquired eagerly. "Your face and garments have black powder specks on them. What was it like in the streets by the mill? We rolled in our *pu-gai*, but could not sleep. The night has been red and gold with firecracker lights—little ones that went *ts! bah! ts-s-s-s-s!* and great ones like this"—she rumbled low in her throat. "Did you see them? And where is Mother?"

Big Sister forced a weary smile. "Mother will come later; then we shall eat."

The younger of the two boys complained, "Small Sister forgot the fire and the rice is cold. I want my rice!" His lower lip began to quiver.

Big Brother frowned at him. "You are a baby! Peach Blossom was talking with the yellow butterfly about its feast of firecrackers. How could she listen to him and care also for the fire?"

Big Sister pushed back weariness and rose to her feet. "I will start a new fire," she comforted, "and by the time Mother comes, the rice will be hot." She began to poke at the small clay stove. She would use a few tea leaves from Mother's special box and flavor their customary drink of hot water. Surely Mother would not scold—at the farm they would have tea often.

Peach Blossom stood rubbing one foot against the other ankle. "May we go to the window again?"

Big Sister nodded permission. Even if the airplane were still up there in the sky, it could not fly in their window, she told herself. With delight the children watched the machine swoop past. Peach Blossom waved an airy smile in its direction. "How large my butterfly has grown this morning!"

The older boy gazed at her with a serious expression. "I think he looks more like a bird."

"This morning—yes. Tomorrow he may be a pink lotus, or a fierce, striped tiger. A wonderful butterfly he is—the emperor of all butterflies—and today is his birthday; that is why the firecrackers are dropping. He told me—" she glanced from the window again, "listen while I sing what he said!" Her words slipped into tuneful rime.

Big Sister, collecting bits of straw and charcoal to start a new fire, half smiled at the nonsense, and wished that Mother would come. The noise was lessening, and except for smoke and the droning of the airplane in the sky, this might be almost any morning here in the grain merchant's room. As she lifted the rice pot, a sudden roar deafened her. Crazily the walls of the room began to dance and darkness followed.

When Big Sister awoke, pain engulfed her. She must have fallen asleep, and the forewoman was punishing her again. A child's cry cleared her brain. Peach Blossom was muttering about a butterfly. Then this was not the mill. Where was she? "Mother! Peach Blossom!" she called, but her voice made no sound. Her mouth filled slowly with thick fluid. After a while, she tried anew for speech. Again the silence remained unbroken. If only she could get up! She twisted there beneath a broken crossbeam and once more blackness swallowed her. Gradually responsibility pulled her back to another moment of consciousness. The fire—she must make the fire! The children were hungry; their rice was cold and the tea was not yet brewed. What must she remember to tell Peach Blossom? A yellow butterfly—a yellow—*ai!* the butterfly must not go to the mill—it would surely fall into a vat!

Her eyelids flickered in a final movement, and the childish lips suddenly relaxed from pain and care———There in the doorway of the little farm stood Peach Blossom leaning against the familiar *mei-hwa* tree, and poised above her on a flowering spray, a great, yellow butterfly opened and closed his wings in the sunlit air.

Now all was well. With a smile of ineffable peace, Big Sister went home to join her ancestors.

CHINESE WORDS

ABACUS (ăb'ȧ-kŭs), a device used for counting, consisting of beads or balls strung on wires, set in a frame

AI-YA (ī-yä), an exclamation expressing surprise, dismay, and sometimes, anger

AMAH (ä'mȧ), an Oriental term for a child's nurse

ASCENDED THE DRAGON, a Chinese term for death

BLACK DWARFS, a term of contempt for Japanese

CHI (chē), the numeral, seven

CHIHLI (jŭ-lē'), a province in northeastern China

CHI KO FAN MO? (chē gō fȧn mŭh), a greeting, meaning "Have you eaten?"

CHOP-CHOP (chŏp-chŏp), pidgin English, meaning fast, swiftly

CHUNGKING (chōong'kĭng'), an important port on the Upper Yangtze, 1500 miles inland

COMPRADOR (kŏm'prȧ-dôr'), (Portuguese for buyer), a native purchasing agent in a foreign business house

COOLIE (kōō'lĭ), a Chinese laborer

ER (ẽr), the numeral, two

FACE, used as a synonym for reputation, or prestige

FILATURE, a place where silk is reeled

FOREST OF PENS, a Chinese term for the Official Examination Halls

FUKIEN (fōō'kyĕn'), a coastal province in south China

GINKGO (gĭngk'gō), an ornamental tree with fan-shaped leaves

GODOWN (gō-doun'), a warehouse

GOLDEN LILIES, the poetical name given to bound feet

HAT-A-MEN (hŏt-ȧ-mŭn), a street in Peiping

HSIEN-SENG (shĕn-sŭng), a title, meaning teacher or gentleman

ICHANG (ē'chăng'), a port on the Yangtze, one thousand miles from Shanghai

KIUKIANG (kyōō'kyăng'), a port city on the Yangtze about four hundred miles from Shanghai

KOBE (kō'bĕ), a Pacific port in Japan

KWAI-TZ (kwī-tz), the Chinese for chopsticks

KUAN-YIN (gwăn-yĭn), goddess of mercy

KWEICHOW (gwā'jō'), a southwestern province in China

KULING (gōō'lĭng), a mountain resort above Kiukiang on the Yangtze

KUSHAN (gōō'săn), a Buddhist mountain resort in Fukien

LA-IH-KO (lä-ē-go), Who is it?

LAO BAN (lou-băn), a manager or proprietor

LAO DAH (lou-dȧ), one in charge of a boat's crew

LI (lē), one third of a mile

LUH (lōō), the numeral, six

MEI-HWA (mā-huā), a pink, flowering shrub

MIDDLE KINGDOM, translation of Chinese name characters for their country

MIXED COURT, the court presided over by representatives from all foreign nations in International Settlement, Shanghai, when foreigners are tried

MUH IU FA TZ (mŭ yōō fä dz), a phrase, meaning "there is no help for it" or "have no other plan"

MOTO-MATCHI (mō-tō-mä-chē), a business thoroughfare in Kobe

NAN-CHING (năn-jĭng), Chinese pronunciation for Nanking

PIDGIN ENGLISH, a form of English based on Chinese with additions from Portuguese and other languages

PU-GAI (pōō-gī), a comfort stuffed with cotton, wool, or silk waste

SAMPAN (săm'păn), a small, flat-bottomed boat propelled by oars, and sometimes, sails

SAN (săn), the numeral, three

SHI, SHI (shė, shė), yes, yes

SI (sė), the numeral, four

SI-MU (sĭ-moo), Chinese for "mistress" or "married woman"

SHORT-LEGGED ONES, a term of contempt for Japanese

SIKH (sēk), a member of a warlike Hindu sect many of whom are enlisted in the British army and used for police duty

CHINESE WORDS

SON OF THE SEA, a name for the Lower Yangtze

SOOCHOW (so͞o'chou'), a city famous for its natural beauty and culture, on the lower Yangtze

SPITTING-BLOOD DISEASE, a descriptive term sometimes used to refer to cholera, sometimes to tuberculosis

SZECHUEN (sė̄'chuän), an extremely large province in west and southwest China

TSAI-HWEI (tsī-hwā), Chinese for good-by; more literally "meet again"

TWO-HUNDRED-CASH WOMAN, a harlot

THROUGH THE GATE, an expression denoting that a bride has left her own home for her husband's

WANCHEE (wan-chē), a pidgin-English term, meaning "wish" or "want," and a typical misuse of verbs by adding "ee"

WAN-WAN (wȧn-wȧn), to play; to use leisure in recreation and entertainment

WHANGPOO (hwȧng-po͞o), the river on which Shanghai is located

WU (wo͞o), the numeral, five

YA-MEN (yä'-mĕ̆n), a Chinese court, police station, or official residence

OLD METHOD OF RECKONING TIME

Hour of the Rat—11 P. M. to 1 A. M.
Hour of the Ox—1 A. M. to 3 A. M.
Hour of the Tiger—3 A. M. to 5 A. M.
Hour of the Hare—5 A. M. to 7 A. M.
Hour of the Dragon—7 A. M. to 9 A. M.
Hour of the Serpent—9 A. M. to 11 A. M.
Hour of the Horse—11 A. M. to 1 P. M.
Hour of the Sheep—1 P. M. to 3 P. M.
Hour of the Monkey—3 P. M. to 5 P. M.
Hour of the Cock—5 P. M. to 7 P. M.
Hour of the Dog—7 P. M. to 9 P. M.
Hour of the Pig—9 P. M. to 11 P. M.

Acknowledgment is made to the following periodicals in which some of these stories were first printed:

High School Publications, American Red Cross
The Classmate
Everywoman's, London
The London *Evening News*
S. T. B., Oslo, Norway

Appreciation is expressed to the publishers for permission to use copyrighted material:

THE CLARENDON PRESS for selection from Ksun K'uang in the Appendix to *Prolegomena* from the *Chinese Classics* translated by James Legge.

THE JOHN DAY COMPANY, INC., for selection from *The Importance of Living* by Lin Yu-tang.

GROSSET & DUNLAP, INC., for selections from *The Travels of Marco Polo.*

The text of this book was set on the monotype machine in 10 point and 11 point Old Style on 16 point body, and printed on Olde Style paper. The typography and design are by William E. Cash, of the Winston Staff. The type was set, and the book printed and bound at the manufactory of The John C. Winston Company, Philadelphia

克士廉